W9-CZM-360

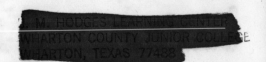

THE
CANCER
LADY

First edition

Library of Congress Cataloging in Publication Data

McCoy, Joseph J
  The cancer lady.

  Includes index.
    1. Cancer—Genetic aspects. 2. Cancer research—
United States—History. 3. Slye, Maud, 1879–1954.
4. Zoologists—United States—Biography. I. Title.
RC268.4.M3   616.9'94'0420924   [B]   77-12571
ISBN 0–8407–6552–5

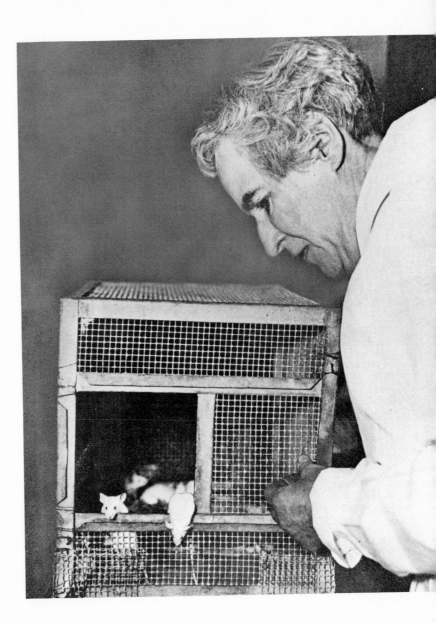

THE CANCER LA
Maud Slye and Her Heredity S

J.J. McCoy

THOMAS NELSON INC., PUBLISHERS
Nashville   New York

To researchers everywhere
who must be allowed to experiment and fail,
if necessary,
in the crusade to conquer cancer.

Author's Note

Though it tells the story of Dr. Maud Slye (1879–1954), this book is not a biography in the usual sense. It is above all the story of cancer research, and Maud Slye's untiring quest into the relationship between cancer and heredity. It is a narrative documentary about a dedicated and talented scientist and her work, which spanned more than thirty-eight years. It is the testimony of a courageous woman, and of her ideas and theories about the causes of cancer. And it is an account of the frustrations, disappointments, emotions, criticisms, prejudices, jealousies, and triumphs that were a part of scientific research at the beginning of the twentieth century.

In telling the story of Maud Slye and her work, I have taken dramatic liberty as far as the narrative thread is concerned, an action which, I hope, may be conceded to be the right of the storyteller. But I have not tampered with the facts. And in accumulating the facts, I have become indebted to a number of persons and organizations.

Accordingly, I wish to thank the Curator of Special Collections, the Joseph Regenstein Library, University of Chicago, for copies of the Maud Slye correspondence; the Roscoe B. Jackson Memorial Laboratory for information on the life and works of Clarence Cook Little, former director of the Laboratory and contemporary of Maud Slye, *Newsweek* for permission to quote from articles and to reproduce photos of Maud Slye and her mice, which appeared in a 1937 issue of the magazine; the American Cancer Society for data on cancer research; *Time* magazine for permission to quote from an article about Maud Slye and Clarence Cook Little; the *Chicago Daily News* for sending clippings about Maud Slye and giving permission to quote same; the *Journal of the American Medical Association;* the *Journal of Cancer Research;* the American Medical Association for a copy of the citation for Maud Slye's Gold Medal; Frank J. Orland, D.D.S., Ph.D., president, American Academy of the History of Dentistry, for his recollections of Maud Slye; and Margot Siegel, reference librarian, Hunterdon County, New Jersey, Library, for her patience and tireless efforts in obtaining the various scientific papers and other research material necessary to write this documentary about Maud Slye.

I am especially grateful to the New Jersey State Council on the Arts for a fellowship that enabled me to complete this work.

—J. J. McCOY
Frenchtown, New Jersey

This is the work that I was set to do,
    And could it seem,
For a transcendent dream,
    I could forsake to see it finished through?

              —Maud Slye

ONE

Maud Slye, newly appointed assistant to Professor Charles Whitman, head of the biology department at the University of Chicago, sat on a stool and stared at two mice in a cage. She was a slight woman with a high forehead and a prominent nose, and her thick hair was cut short, so that it just barely reached below her ears. Her white laboratory coat was almost a size too large for her, and the wide collar lay back on her shoulders like the cowl of a monk's robe when not in use. But Maud was not concerned with her looks or with the ill-fitting laboratory coat. What held her attention were the mice in the cage.

The mice were no ordinary rodents. They were Japanese waltzing mice, and Maud had purchased them with her own money. Waltzing mice were not a new phenomenon to scientists of the early twentieth century. These strange little rodents were known in China many centuries ago. Eventually, Japan and other countries obtained waltzing mice from China and developed their own strains. Until recently, the mice had been regarded as nothing more than animal oddities, little creatures exhibited for the amusement of people. But some scientists had become interested in them and conducted studies aimed at discovering the cause of their whirling locomotion.

The scientists who studied the waltzing mice were mainly geneticists, biologists who were concerned with heredity and with variations in animals and plants. After long research, the geneticists discovered that the waltzing mice behaved as they did because of a nervous disarrangement. Furthermore, they believed that the disarrangement was inherited. Ultimately, after more studies, the geneticists learned that the waltzing motion, the head-tossing, and the general hyperactivity of the dancing mice were recessive characters. That is, the characters were dormant, or latent, and were capable of development or appearance in new generations of mice under certain conditions.

Maud watched the strange movements of her two waltzing mice. They did not creep or scamper around the cage like other mice. Instead, they moved or danced in circles, constantly tossing their heads and gyrating around the cage like miniature dervishes. Maud wanted to know more about their behavior. She knew that their peculiar waltzing motion was considered to be an inherited trait. But what factors were involved? Why did the mice behave as they did?

To find the answer to these and other genetic questions was the reason Maud had purchased the waltzing mice. She was interested in isolating the different factors involved in the inheritance of nervous disorders. The Japanese waltzing mice would be excellent subjects for such a study because their curious locomotion would be relatively easy to recognize in future generations. She planned to breed the waltzing mice with normal white mice and to keep meticulous records on the matings and the resultant litters of young and, subsequently, on the families and strains of mice developed from the original matings.

In keeping with this plan, Maud had purchased some normal white mice from Abby Lathrop, a mouse fancier in Granby, Massachusetts. These white mice and the Japanese waltzing mice made up the basic stock for her proposed mouse-research project. While she did not know it at the time, she had started a most ambitious research venture, one that would involve her for the rest of her life.

Maud's interest in nervous disorders stemmed from something that had happened to her when she was an undergraduate in college. She had entered the University of Chicago as a freshman in 1895, and there were problems right from the start.

In the beginning, it had been doubtful whether Maud would go to college at all. Her parents, James Alvin and Florence Alden Slye, were poor and had no money to pay for Maud's college education. If she wanted to go to the University of Chicago, as she most certainly did, then she had to find a way to earn some money. Her parents would contribute what little they could to her education, but Maud would have to make up the difference.

Quiet, reserved, and highly intelligent, Maud was determined that she would go to college. She was deeply interested in music, art, nature, and psychology. She also had the determination, dedication, and studious mind that were necessary for the successful scholar or scientist. Whatever her attributes, she knew that what she wanted in life had to begin with college. Therefore, she enrolled at the University of Chicago, determined to find some way to earn the necessary board and tuition. Fortunately, she was hired as a clerk in the office of William Rainey Harper, president of the University of Chicago. Although her wages were barely enough to pay for her tuition and keep her alive, the job in President Harper's office made the difference between going to college and not going to college.

For three years, Maud did her work in President Harper's office and at the same time carried a full load of academic courses. The combination of clerical work and college classes was a heavy burden for the young, sensitive woman, but there was nothing she could do but work and study if she wanted to remain at the university. Women were a minority in the university; in fact, they were a minority in most coeducational colleges and universities. Few scholarships were available to women, and no rich relatives came forth to ease

Maud's load. Although she managed to do her clerical work and maintain a good average in her courses, the work proved too much for her. In the spring of 1898, she suffered what people politely called a "nervous breakdown." As a result of the breakdown, Maud was obliged to leave the university.

Maud sought medical help, and her physician advised her to take time off, to leave the university and go somewhere to regain her health. Maud had relatives in Massachusetts, and she decided to go to them and try to restore her shattered nerves. Rest, of course, was what she needed, but after a month of rest and relaxation, she needed to use her mind again—to think, to study, and to pursue some project. She was able to take some courses at the Woods Hole Laboratory. This time, however, she did not overload herself, and she was able to study with less strain on her nerves.

By the fall of 1898, Maud was well enough to enter Brown University and then to finish the requirements for her bachelor's degree. Later, she accepted a position as a psychology teacher at the Rhode Island Normal School. Her work at the Normal School—an institution that trained teachers in two years—introduced her to the fields of genetics and psychiatry. She soon developed an interest in human heredity and began to learn all she could about this fascinating young field of science.

At the time that Maud became absorbed in genetics, a bitter controversy was raging between geneticists and biometricians over the relative merits and correct methodology of genetic research. The science of genetics was just beginning to emerge as a discipline. More scientists were taking a second look at the work and conclusions of Gregor Mendel, the Austrian monk who had conducted experiments on heredity with hybrid plants. The results of Mendel's experiments had been published in 1866, but they had been cast aside and ignored until 1900, at which time three scientists corroborated Mendel's conclusions on recessive and dominant characteristics.

But the biometricians, scientists who applied statistical methods to biological facts, and who advocated mathematical analysis of biological data, were not convinced that the conclusions of Mendel and other geneticists were valid. And so the controversy went on.

Maud Slye, because of her interest in human heredity, joined the controversy on the side of the geneticists. Even though genetics was a new field for her, she managed to make an impression on Professor Charles Whitman, who had founded the Woods Hole Laboratory. Whitman admired Maud's keen, analytical mind, her dedication to an idea, and her disciplined approach to her work. When Whitman accepted the position as head of the biology department at the University of Chicago, he suggested to Maud that she come to the university as his graduate assistant. Maud agreed, and was given a small fellowship, which barely paid for her room and board. She was also given a corner of the basement in the Zoology Building as her laboratory.

For her postgraduate research project, Maud elected to investigate the factors involved in the inheritance of nervous abnormalities. It is more than likely that her own nervous problem influenced her choice of a research project. The nervous breakdown she had suffered as an undergraduate at the university had intensified her interest in psychology and psychiatry, and the possible relationship between heredity and nervous disorders fitted into the new field of genetics. At any rate, Maud launched her research into the causes of nervous disorders with her Japanese waltzing mice and the white mice she had obtained from Abby Lathrop in Massachusetts.

Mice are prolific breeders, so Maud's colony expanded rapidly. Soon the small, cramped laboratory in the basement of the Zoology Building began to fill up with mouse cages. Maud kept placing the cages in tiers that reached almost to the ceiling, but finally, when her mouse colony numbered more than a hundred individuals, she asked for a larger laboratory.

More space was found for her mice and equipment on the third floor of the Zoology Building. Here, without the help of any assistant, she pursued her studies of the mice, doing all the work herself: cleaning cages, feeding the mice, sterilizing equipment, and carefully recording all of her observations. She often worked eighteen hours a day in the mouse laboratory, almost as though time had no meaning. Only when she was completely exhausted did she close up the laboratory and go to her room in the boardinghouse.

Although the university sanctioned Maud's mouse-research project, it gave her no funds to carry out her work, and she had to make out the best way she could. Consequently, she had to pay all the laboratory expenses out of her meager fellowship funds. Because she had to feed her mice, there were days when she ate very little herself, and days when she went without eating altogether so that she could provide her precious mice with hay and grain. She lived a spartan life, totally dedicated to her work, and did not complain of the hardships or demand a higher salary. Her work was all that mattered, and if going to bed hungry was the price she had to pay to do it, then that was the way it would be.

One day Dr. John Watson, the director of the university's comparative psychology research project, visited Maud Slye's mouse laboratory. Watson had heard about the "Mouse Lady" and her laboratory on the third floor of the Zoology Building. He was curious about Maud and the work she was doing with the constantly growing colony of laboratory mice. Maud escorted Dr. Watson around her unusual laboratory, pointing out the different mice and generations of mice. She explained the nature of her research project and displayed the detailed charts she kept on the mice. Watson was impressed by Maud's careful research methods. He asked her how she managed to take care of all the mice herself and how she was able to feed them all. Maud told him that she had no assistant and that she had to buy the food for the mice out of her fellowship money.

Dr. Watson shook his head. He knew the pitifully small salary that graduate assistants received, and he could not believe that Maud was able to maintain herself and her mice on what the university paid her. Yet the evidence was all around him. Somehow—and the behavorial scientist guessed that it was through self-denial—the slight, serious woman had managed to keep herself and her mice alive on the pittance paid by the university.

Watson was moved by Maud's dedication and determination. He offered her food supplies from his department, telling her that she could have as much milk and bread as she needed for her mice. Maud thanked him in a low voice, for she was suddenly filled with emotion. This was the first time that anyone had offered to help out with her project since she came to the university.

Maud was on the bottom rung of the scientific ladder in the university. First, she was a woman. There were few woman scientists in the United States at the turn of the century. The scientific establishment was a masculine field, and the men who dominated it did not think that women belonged in the field. Those few women who did manage to gain a toehold in the scientific community were rarely given the same opportunities as men. What is more, female scientists were generally paid lower salaries than men who performed the same work.

When Maud started her mouse laboratory, the Woman's Suffrage Movement, pioneered by militant women such as Susan Brownell Anthony, had two fronts: the American Women Suffrage Association, which worked to eliminate discriminatory laws against women at the state level; and the National Women's Suffrage Association, which campaigned for equal rights for women by way of a constitutional amendment. Most suffragettes believed that the best way to achieve equal rights for women was to obtain the right to vote. But for

Maud Slye and other women scientists, relegated to a minor position in a male-dominated scientific establishment, equality was a long way off.

Despite her lowly position in the scientific community and her lack of funds, Maud went on with her mouse research, carefully breeding mice and keeping meticulous records on them. She continued to put in long hours at the laboratory, but the strain of her work was not the same as that which she had endured as an undergraduate. True, her work was exacting, but she had no boss to please and no examinations to badger her. What she was doing now was what she wanted to do, and she became totally absorbed in her research. Her dedication to the long project she had created for herself was exceeded only by the stern discipline she practiced.

Her study of the nervous disorders of the Japanese waltzing mice and the ability of the waltzers to transmit their dancing locomotion to their offspring proceeded slowly. There was no hurrying such a project. Time was needed to produce strains of mice that were or were not susceptible to the dizzying movement of the waltzers.

Meanwhile, as her mouse colony grew larger and she amassed more data, Maud became interested in the work of a young scientist named Leo Loeb. Loeb was a pathologist who was conducting a study of the endemic incidence of cancer. Endemic cancer is a disease that seems to have a low rate of occurrence, but which constantly persisted or prevails in certain communities. Loeb wanted to learn why cancer was endemic in a given community. As part of his research project, he had examined a number of slaughtered cattle in a Chicago slaughterhouse; some of the cattle had been afflicted with cancer of the eye. What interested Loeb was that the affected cattle had all come from one ranch in Wyoming. These cattle posed an interesting question: were they the result of an endemic occurrence of cancer, or were they a strain of cattle with a hereditary tendency to cancer?

After Loeb's study of the cattle with eye cancer, he turned

his attention to what appeared to be an endemic occurrence of cancer in three laboratory rats. The rats, which lived in separate but adjacent cages, all suffered from cancer of the thyroid gland. Loeb thought the thyroid cancer might be caused by a hereditary factor rather than by infection. However, he could not prove his theory. More study was needed before a conclusion could be drawn. Furthermore, what was required was a long-range breeding experiment with mice and rats to determine the cause of cancer in mammals. Loeb later examined mice in Abby Lathrop's colony and found that cancer was more prevalent in certain strains of mice raised by her. This time, Loeb announced that cancer in mammals was probably related to some hereditary factor.

Another pathologist, Ernest Tyzzer at Harvard Medical School, was thinking along the same lines as Loeb, and he published a paper on the inheritance of cancer in mice. In his paper, Tyzzer pointed out the high frequency of tumors in the lungs of mice. He believed that heredity was an important factor in the incidence of mouse cancer, but how and to what extent he did not know.

In England, members of the Royal Society of Medicine also considered the possibility that heredity might be a factor in cancer. But the Society was by no means unified on the theory. Some members believed in it; others stated that nobody had ever conducted a lengthy study of the problem and that therefore no reliable data existed.

What was needed, of course, was a carefully controlled mouse-breeding program to establish whether heredity was or was not a factor in cancer. As yet there was no such program, but the idea intrigued Maud Slye. In her mouse laboratory were the basic ingredients for such a research project. She had a growing colony of mice, and records on their background. Her research could easily be switched from the study of inheritance factors in nervous disarrangements to a study of the possible relationship between cancer and heredity.

The more she thought about it, the more interested she

became in the possibilities of such an extended breeding program. Then she made up her mind to do it. She would center her research around the possibility that spontaneous cancers in mice were related to some unknown hereditary factor, and she would conduct it along the same lines as those used by geneticists who experimented with the inheritance of immediately observable characteristics, such as coat and eye colors in mice and rats.

But Maud did not intend to begin her research project with any preconceived notions or theories, nor would she tamper with any spontaneous tumors that developed in her mice. That method would lead to false results and conclusions. What she intended to do was to see what happened when she crossed large numbers of cancerous mice with noncancerous mice.

Maud's proposed project was a tremendous undertaking, and she realized it would take years of study. Whatever conclusions she drew from her research would have to be based on the results of thousands of matings, not just a few. Other scientists, especially the skeptical biometricians, would demand conclusions based on research involving many generations of mice. Otherwise, they would reject her work.

At the time that Maud began to breed mice for spontaneous tumors, Professor Thomas Hunt Morgan was breeding *Drosophila*, the fruit fly, in genetic experiments at Columbia University. Morgan's work was extremely important, for it eventually established the structure of genetics. The behavior of many traits in animals and plants had previously been reported more or less in accordance with the hereditary rules set down by Gregor Mendel. But the work of Morgan and his associates at Columbia University showed that the inherited trait involved in his study was linked—and not limited, as scientists originally believed—to the determination of the sex of the particular fruit fly. Morgan was awarded the Nobel Prize for physiology and medicine in 1933.

A new inherited trait in fruit flies, discovered by Morgan, was a white eye color, as contrasted with the usual red eye color. Earlier experiments had demonstrated that in other insects sex was determined by the presence of specific chromosomes—the easily detected bodies in each cell nucleus that contained the hereditary units or genes. What excited geneticists about the fruit fly's genetic makeup was that all of the fly's genes were contained on only four pairs of chromosomes. One of the four pairs of chromosomes carried genes that affected the eye and wing colors of the fruit fly and, in addition, determined the sex of the developing fly. This pair of chromosomes determined sex by altering the balance of the genetic structure of the organism.

What all of this meant was that genetic research, such as that conducted by Professor Morgan and his students at Columbia University, might provide the clue as to the origin of cancer. This was the basis on which Maud Slye conducted her research with mice. However, Professor Morgan had a decided advantage over Maud Slye when it came to the subjects involved in the research. The fruit fly was easily maintained under laboratory conditions. More important, fruit flies reproduced more rapidly than Maud Slye's mice. A new generation of *Drosophila* appeared in a day or so, while mice required nineteen days from fertilization to birth of the young. Also, mice grew more slowly, reaching maturity at about sixty days. Therefore, Maud could not expect the relatively quick results obtained by Professor Morgan. Her experiments would have to proceed at a much slower rate.

Undaunted by the enormity of her research project, Maud went on breeding her mice. Soon a mouse developed cancer of the breast. Then another mouse developed breast tumors, and after that, more spontaneous tumors appeared in her mice. They were called spontaneous tumors because they had not been grafted into the mice but had developed naturally. Eventually, Maud had the first litter of baby mice born to a cancerous mother. She looked at the tiny, squirming babies, pink and hairless, and knew that now she had the material to determine whether or not cancer was inherited.

But the baby mice from a cancerous mother were only the beginning. More and more matings were necessary, as was the need to produce strains of cancerous and noncancerous mice, carefully tabulating the results. Such a project would take a long time. Moreover, it would take funds. If she was to get any money for her project, she would have to have the support of the university.

Maud took the matter to her department head. She showed him the baby mice born to a cancerous mother. "Here," she declared, "is the material to determine whether or not cancer is inherited."

The department head was impressed by the offspring of the cancerous mouse. He regarded the birth of the mice as an achievement in itself, especially since cancer was a lethal disease. However, he was not interested in a research project aimed at finding a link between cancer and heredity, and he turned down Maud's request. "That question was settled a long time ago," he told her. "Cancer is not inherited."

Maud refused to have the subject dismissed so summarily. Only a research project such as the one she envisioned would provide the answer as to whether cancer was an inheritable disease or not. She thought about it for a few days, wondering how and where she could conduct the necessary research. Then she decided to approach Dr. Ludvig Hektoen, the head of the pathology department. Dr. Hektoen listened patiently while Maud talked about her growing mouse colony and about how she would like to use her mice in a prolonged study to determine whether a relationship existed between cancer and heredity.

Dr. Hektoen nodded thoughtfully from time to time. Then Maud asked the question that would decide the course of her future research. "Dr. Hektoen, has it been definitely established that cancer is not an inheritable disease?"

The pathologist shook his head. "No, it is far from being settled. There is not even anyone who has the material to settle it." He looked pointedly at her. "Unless you have."

Maud returned the look. "I think I do," she replied.

Dr. Hektoen smiled at her. "Then you have my permission to go ahead."

Maud was elated. She now had permission to conduct a research project on a scale never before attempted by any scientist. But she still needed money. To raise thousands of mice would require funds for equipment and a salary for an assistant. She mentioned this to Dr. Hektoen, and he promised to see what could be done to obtain the necessary money for Maud's project.

Unfortunately the mechanism for securing funds at the university was complicated and subject to politics and approvals from a variety of people. The funding of Maud's project, assuming it was approved, might take months. She did not want to wait that long. Although it would be difficult, Maud decided to go ahead with her project, even though it meant defraying expenses with her scanty salary. All she could do was hope that Dr. Hektoen would get her the money, not for herself but for her mice and for the research that she believed could provide an answer to the cancer question.

However, the funds did not appear. Maud waited patiently, but she did not lose any valuable time. She spent most of her time in the mouse laboratory, vigorously scrubbing cages and equipment, and feeding her insatiable mice. She mated cancerous mice with cancerous mice, and cancerous mice with noncancerous mice. She knew every mouse in her laboratory. When a mouse died, she conducted an autopsy to learn why the mouse died. If there was a tumor, she noted the type, site, and whether it was benign or malignant. Her records and charts multiplied. And as the work load became heavier and heavier, she wondered if she would ever receive the money to go on with her research. Until then, all she could do was to keep on working.

In her small laboratory, surrounded by several hundred mice, Maud Slye sought the answer to the question: Is cancer an inheritable disease? It was a trying period of her life when, as she expressed it in later years, she managed to "hang on by her teeth."

TWO

Maud's early research into the possible relationship between cancer and heredity was conducted in relative obscurity. Although cancer was a dreaded disease that killed thousands of Americans each year, and one for which the cause was as yet unknown, there was no public spotlight turned on the mouse laboratory in the University of Chicago's Zoology Building. Furthermore, only a few scientists even thought that there might be a link between cancer and heredity. Consequently, Maud worked alone and with no funds other than her fellowship money.

Then, in 1911, Maud got the break she had hoped for. Otho S. A. Sprague, an extremely wealthy man, died and left millions of dollars for medical research. The Sprague Memorial Institute was established at the University of Chicago, and an eminent pathologist, H. Gideon Wells, was appointed director. Maud Slye was named to the Institute staff and was permitted to go ahead with her cancer research. Now, for the first time, she was given a salary and a laboratory large enough for her to work in comfort and ease. Still, there was no money for an assistant.

By this time, Maud's mouse colony had outgrown the small space allocated to her on the third floor of the Zoology Building. She now had nearly a thousand mice in hundreds of cages. She asked for larger quarters for her mice and equipment and was given the use of an old two-story building on the edge of the university campus. In the new quarters, mouse cages continued to dominate, leaving barely enough room for desks, laboratory tables, file cabinets and other equipment. The first impression of a visitor to these new quarters was of shabbiness and congestion. But a closer look soon showed that there was orderliness and organization in Maud's new mouse laboratory, despite all of the cages and equipment that seemed to engulf the rooms.

Maud kept adding more cages that she designed, fitting them on top of each other with a small space between the bottom of one cage and the top of another. Yet each cage was readily accessible, both for the quick observation of the mice inhabitants and for easy and efficient cleaning. If there was one procedure Maud never changed or delegated, it was the cleaning of the cages. First of all, she had no assistant and had to do all the work herself. Secondly, sanitation was a crucial element in the maintenance of the mouse colony. There was always the danger of some contagious disease sweeping from mouse to mouse and cage to cage, and an epidemic of disease could wipe out her mouse colony and years of work. Therefore—even though it required long hours—Maud painstakingly cleaned all of the mouse cages and catered to the needs of the mice.

Gradually, Maud's mice and the work she was doing with them attracted the attention of some university faculty members and the staff of the Sprague Memorial Institute. Of course, a great deal of curiosity arose about what went on in the mouse laboratory in the old building on the edge of the campus. There was also mounting interest in the "Mouse Lady," the small, quiet, and dedicated woman who spent most of her time with the squeaking mice in the cages that were piled nearly to the ceiling. What was she doing with all those mice? And what was she trying to discover?

One day, Maud had a visitor. It was Harriet Holmes, a woman of culture and independent means who was also a trained pathologist. Miss Holmes was fascinated by Maud's laboratory and the mouse colony. She listened attentively while Maud explained her research, pointing out individual mice and the steadily growing families and strains of mice. Miss Holmes was amazed when she learned that Maud was the sole human occupant of the laboratory, conducting all the research and caring for all the mice herself. She asked Maud why there was no laboratory assistant.

"There are no funds for an assistant," replied Maud.

"But you need help in here!"

Maud nodded and gently picked up a mouse. "Yes, I could use some help." She smiled wanly at Miss Holmes. "But I am used to doing everything myself."

"I would like to help you," offered Miss Holmes.

Maud placed the mouse into its cage. "I cannot pay you."

"I don't need to be paid," replied Miss Holmes. "I have a source of money. I would like to be useful—and I would love to work here."

"That is generous of you," said Maud.

"Where do you need help most of all?"

"To be truthful, I can use help with the tissue slides."

"Then," said Miss Holmes, "let me make them up for you. I have worked with tissue slides before."

"All right, Miss Holmes. I am delighted to have you as my assistant. You can make up the tissue slides and I will check them under the microscope." She paused. "Perhaps I can persuade Dr. Wells to check them also."

Gideon Wells agreed to work with Maud on all her microscopic analyses of tissues from mice that died. If Wells checked her tissue work, other scientists would not ignore or dismiss her diagnoses. Wells offered to make a most important contribution to Maud's research. He was not only the director of the Sprague Memorial Institute, but a highly esteemed pathologist. Few scientists would arbitrarily dismiss his corroboration of Maud Slye's mouse-tissue analysis.

Aided by Harriet Holmes as laboratory assistant and for-
tified by the expertise of Gideon Wells, Maud increased the
scope of her laboratory work. While Miss Holmes prepared
the tissue slides, Maud examined them under the microscope,
noting which tissues were cancerous and which were not. At
the time that Maud started her cancer research, cancer was
rated sixth as the cause of death among human beings. The
main reason cancer was so far down the scale as a cause of
human death was that the diagnosis of the disease was not
very accurate. Also, people did not live as long as they do
today; therefore, fewer people reached the age at which most
cancers develop. This factor had a definite bearing on what
few statistics existed on the disease.

Of course cancer in human beings had been known for
centuries. In the fifth century B.C., Hippocrates, the Greek
physician, used the Greek word for crab when he described
the spreading growths he found in human and animal bodies.
But it was the Romans who called these body growths cancers.
By 1900, it was known that cancer begins as a simple body cell
or group of cells that suddenly start to multiply without any
restraint. The cells grow independently of the rest of the body,
invading the surrounding tissues or organs. This invasion is
accomplished by direct contact or by spreading throughout
the body when a small group of cells breaks off from the main
or primary growth. When they do break off, they are carried to
distant tissues and organs by the blood or lymph channels.
Such spreading, or transmission, is known as *metastasis*.

Pathologists distinguish malignant tumors from benign
tumors by studying tissue samples under the microscope.
Furthermore, noncancerous tumors differ from cancerous
tumors in that they do not metastasize or invade other tissues
or organs. Noncancerous tumors usually grow slowly, and
they interfere with function only by exerting pressure or by
obstructing the surrounding structures. Finally, benign
tumors can threaten life when they grow so large that they
compress some vital organ or structure.

In spite of the research that had been conducted on cancer by Maud Slye's time, the cause of this terrible disease was unknown. The ancient Greeks and Romans thought that it was caused by the "humoral imbalance of the body." Humors were any fluids or semifluids in the bodies of animals and human beings. However, in Maud Slye's early research days, scientists had several theories as to the cause of cancer. One theory was that proposed by Julius Friedrich Cohnheim, a German pathologist, who announced his theory more than sixty years before Maud Slye began her research. Cohnheim assumed that tumors started from misplaced embryonic cells; that is, cells that were formed in the fetus before birth. The embryonic cells, according to Cohnheim's theory, remained dormant for years. Then, in later life, some unknown stimulus started the cells' growing at a rapid rate until a malignant tumor resulted. Actually, pathologists had seen the embryonic displacement of cells and accepted the fact that these displaced cells accounted for the start of tumors. But the chief objection to Cohnheim's theory was that tumors could be caused in almost any part of the animal or human body by chronic irritation.

Another and more widely accepted theory was that cancer was caused by the action of some unknown parasite, probably a bacterium. The parasite caused irritation of tissues and invaded the cells, thus causing them to multiply or grow at a rapid rate. In the latter part of the nineteenth century, a scientist had isolated bacteria from a breast tumor. He then injected the bacteria into some dogs. The dogs, according to the scientist, developed breast cancer.

It was true that various bacteria had been taken from cancerous tissues, but further investigation showed that these bacteria actually were *secondary invaders* of the tissues and therefore were not the primary cause of the cancers. Nevertheless, the bacterial theory of cancer was still prevalent when Maud began her research into the possible relationship between cancer and heredity.

Maud realized that she would encounter difficulty in convincing some scientists of even the possibility that cancer was an inheritable disease. The scientific community was divided into two main camps, those who believed that cancer was caused by a contagious organism and those who thought that chronic irritation was the cause.

In addition to the preconceived notions about the cause of cancer, there was the matter of Maud Slye's being a woman scientist. Even scientists who were supposed to be objective were prejudiced when it came to women in the scientific establishment. A number of them were quick to dismiss the work and findings of the few women scientists who were able to get their research published in the medical and scientific journals. Unfair though it was, it was a reality of the times. Maud knew that she would have to work harder and produce irrefutable data, not only because she was experimenting in a highly controversial area, but also because she was a woman. And her chief opponents or critics would be those male scientists who were conducting cancer research.

Once again, Maud's laboratory was threatened with an overflow of mice and cages as her colony kept growing larger. She requested more spacious quarters and was given a three-story building on Drexel Avenue in Chicago, a building that was destined to become both an object of curiosity and controversy. Maud divided the building into sections or departments, according to the needs of her research. In the basement were the various pieces of equipment needed to clean and sterilize the hundreds of mouse cages, water containers, and food dishes. On the first floor, Maud kept the offspring of cancerous mice. The second floor was reserved for all of Maud's cancer-free mice. And the top floor was a miscellaneous section, used for whatever purpose existed at the moment. All of Maud's tissue slides were kept in the university Pathology Building. Each slide had been carefully examined by Maud and then checked by Gideon Wells.

As the generations of mice increased, so did the volume of notes, charts, and other data. Every time a mouse died, Maud conducted an autopsy, carefully examining the tissues and organs of the deceased rodent. If death had been caused by cancer, she recorded the type and location of the tumors. All of her tissue examinations and diagnoses were cross-checked by Harriet Holmes and Gideon Wells. A complete history was kept on each mouse, giving the date of birth, matings, ailments, behavior, and the cause of death. Any change in a mouse's physical condition or its behavior pattern—in fact, any observable change—was recorded for study and interpretation. After three more years of research, which included autopsies on five thousand mice, Maud had accumulated enough data to write her first report on her research into the possible relationship between cancer and heredity.

On May 5, 1913, Maud appeared with her research paper and a number of charts at a meeting of the American Society for Cancer Research. The subject she intended to present at the meeting was "The Incidence and Inheritability of Spontaneous Cancer in Mice." The scientists and physicians attending the meeting were a mixed group, as far as theories on the cause of cancer were concerned. Some of them still adhered to the contagious-disease theory of cancer causation; others persisted in the belief that irritation alone was the cause of cancer. Regardless of their beliefs, they were a very formidable audience for the small, intense woman who faced them with her first scientific report on a possible cause of cancer.

Maud began by describing her research methods and procedures. She told the assembled physicians and scientists that out of the 5,000 mice on which she had conducted autopsies, 298 had cancer. She exhibited a chart that gave the history of a cancerous family of mice. The mating had produced a litter of six young. Two males from the litter eventually died from mammary tumors. Another male was alive at the time Maud delivered her report, and that animal was free from cancer.

One female from the litter died from lung cancer and another, although still alive, had developed mammary tumors. The third female appeared to be noncancerous. All of the tumors developed by the mice shown on the chart were spontaneous tumors; they had grown naturally and had not been grafted into the mice. What the members of the American Society for Cancer Research were looking at was a chart that gave a scientific description of a cancerous family of mice. The fact that cancer showed up in four of the six offspring indicated that both parents were cancerous. Maud explained that a mouse could be called purebreeding noncancerous when it fulfilled three conditions: (1) it died without cancer as shown by autopsy, (2) when mated with a cancerous mate, only cancer-free young were produced, and (3) it was possible to derive an extracted line of wholly cancer-free descendants.

Even those physicians and scientists who did not believe in the inheritance theory of cancer were impressed by what they saw and heard. The magnitude of the research project did not escape them. Who had ever autopsied 5,000 mice? Or kept records on that number? Nobody but this small, quiet woman who stood before them. Even if the results should ultimately prove her to be wrong, she deserved to be complimented for her labors. But there were some discerning scientists who realized that the data on the chart indicated that heredity, not contagion, was a major factor in the incidence of cancer, at least in this particular family of mice.

Maud gave the final blow to the contagion theory. "I have eliminated contagion as a factor in the transmission of cancer," she told the audience. She went on to explain that she had kept some of the cancerous and noncancerous mice in the same cage. Sometimes when a cancerous mouse died, non-cancerous mice had been given the soiled cage with all the litter soiled by the dead mouse. Yet purebreeding noncancerous mice mated with each other in these cages produced noncancerous offspring. She added that a daughter often developed cancer before the mother did and months after the mother and daughter had been placed in separate cages.

Even though the scientists and physicians were impressed by Maud's work, they were not ready to accept the theory that the susceptibility to cancer was inherited. It was a familiar story: science, particularly medicine, was slow to accept new theories without overwhelming proof. Maud Slye's work was interesting—so was her chart and paper—but she was a long way from proving that cancer was an inheritable disease. Science and medicine would wait and see.

Not all scientists and physicians summarily dismissed Maud's work. Her research project, whatever its outcome as far as proving cancer was an inheritable disease, was a tremendous undertaking, a tour-de-force for a single researcher on a minimal salary or stipend, and some physicians thought she should be recognized for her contribution to medical research. At its sixty-fourth annual session, held in June, 1914, in Atlantic City, New Jersey, the American Medical Association gave Maud Slye a gold medal for her mouse-and-cancer exhibit. The AMA Committee on Awards for Scientific Exhibits reported to the general membership as follows:

> That the first prize, the gold medal for the best Scientific Exhibit, be awarded to Miss Maud Slye of the Otho S. A. Sprague Memorial Institute of Chicago, for her exhibit of charts, diagrams, specimens, and tables on the transmission of hereditary cancer and other diseases in mice.
> The Committee wishes further to express its admiration of Miss Slye's work in this field and its appreciation of the great personal sacrifice she has made and for her courtesy in presenting the work before the Association.

The American Medical Association Gold Medal notwithstanding, there were many scientists, particularly those engaged in some form of cancer research, who refused to accept Maud's work and her conclusions. Some of them aired their criticisms in the scientific journals, emphasizing that Maud Slye's work was far from being conclusive. A good deal of the opposition to her work came from members of the American Society for Cancer Research, publisher of the *Journal of Cancer Research* and, more or less, the authoritative organization concerned with cancer research and control.

Challenge and criticism were, of course, to be expected when a new theory was proposed to the scientific world, especially a theory on the cause of cancer. Maud knew this and accepted it. Therefore, she settled down to producing more evidence that cancer was linked with heredity. She came up with evidence that one theory as to the cause of cancer was erroneous. This was the theory that cancer was the result of the action of some kind of toxin on certain tissues and on the body as a whole. A number of cancerous mice in her laboratory developed tumors nearly the size of their bodies, yet these mice lived until death was caused by massive bleeding. Maud stated that if the cancer had been caused by a toxin, as a number of scientists insisted, the mice could never have survived with the tremendous growths for as long as they did. She pointed out that even though mice were delicate animals and highly susceptible to the toxin of typhoid fever, they could and did survive with tumors that were massive in size, in fact, with some tumors that stretched from a mouse's neck to its tail. A cancer toxin, declared Maud, if such did exist, would have killed the mouse very early.

Maud's meticulous research also showed that cancer did not interfere with the normal reproduction process in her mice unless the growth existed in the reproductive organs or appeared in some vital organ. She could document this observation with records on thousands of baby mice born to mothers afflicted with cancer at the time they conceived. Some of the cancerous mouse mothers in her laboratory had as many as seven or eight litters, with up to sixteen babies per litter. Furthermore, the cancerous mothers were able to provide adequate nourishment for their babies. The life span of mice born to cancerous mothers was normal and they, in turn, produced large and healthy litters, unless, of course, they developed cancer and died before reproducing. But Maud found that it was impossible to obtain families of mice from mothers that suffered from other major rodent diseases.

The years passed too quickly for Maud Slye. Her involvement in the long-range cancer research project was total, and it bordered on being an obsession. In fact, there were those scientists who believed that the "Mouse Lady" *was* obsessed, and even possessed, because of her relentless pursuit of the cancer-heredity relationship. They pointed to the long hours Maud spent in her laboratory and to the fact that she had moved into a house just across the street from her mouse laboratory. Such dedication and devotion to a research project were laudable, of course, but a bit on the fanatical side.

True, Maud did spend long hours in the laboratory and she had moved to living quarters across the street from the laboratory. She did not mind the long hours in the laboratory; they were necessary, because in a long-range project, which might be limited only by the life span of the researcher, time was an essential ingredient. As for living across the street from her precious mouse laboratory, Maud had an explanation for that. Her new living quarters were handy to the laboratory and saved her time, for she did not have to travel long distances back and forth to the laboratory. There was only so much time in a day, month, year, and lifetime, and Maud intended to use it wisely.

The picture that some people had of Maud Slye, that of a fanatical female scientist who lived for nothing else but her cancer-research project, was an exaggeration, a distortion. It was quite true that she practically lived in the mouse laboratory, breeding cancerous mice to cancerous mice or cancerous mice to noncancerous mice, watching litters being born to cancerous and noncancerous mouse mothers, observing the cancers developed by her mice, noting that her cancerous mice developed every type and location of cancer known to scientists, and conducting autopsies and miscroscopic examinations of mouse tissue. These things did occupy her day after day and month after month. But there were moments, even a few hours, when she left the mouse laboratory to enter another world.

The minutes and hours that Maud spent away from the mouse laboratory and the exactitude of her research work were precious to her. It was then that she could lie on the spring grass in her yard, feeling the coolness of the grass on her face and the calmness it brought her. She spent hours watching a bird build a nest or carry fat-bodied insects to open-mouthed fledglings. She opened her bedroom window at night to listen to the sounds of the great city of Chicago, or sat in her apartment jotting down her thoughts and dreams in verse. She listened to the sweeping strains of a symphony or the crescendo of the coda of a piano concerto, or plunged her hands into the dark soil in her garden as she prepared it to receive a bulb or root or flower seeds. These were the moments, minutes, and hours when Maud Slye shed the white laboratory coat and stern discipline of the dedicated researcher and became a woman and an artist. And she shared them only with a few friends.

Refreshed by these respites away from the rigors of the laboratory, she would then return to the seemingly endless research and her mice patients. Her absorption with nature and gardening, the purging of her pent-up feelings by writing poetry, and her complete surrender to music—each of these gave her more strength to go on with her research and to meet the criticisms and even hostility that emanated from some scientists. Soon there were more rumblings of discontent with Maud's work and conclusions, more skepticism about her insistence that there was a link between cancer and inheritance. Some scientists were now reporting that their studies and experiments indicted that Maud Slye was not only making conclusions that were not based on facts, but that she was on the wrong trail. A movement seemed to be afoot not only to voice professional criticism of her work, but to discredit her observations and disprove her conclusions. And a few scientists—fundamentalists as far as cancer causation was concerned—tried to render the coup de grace to the whole theory of cancer inheritance.

More cancer research was being conducted now. In Denmark, Johannes Fibiger, a pathologist at the University of Copenhagen, was studying tuberculosis in laboratory animals. A common laboratory animal susceptible to tuberculosis was the rat. Fibiger, while conducting postmortem examinations on three rats that were tubercular, noticed that they had stomach cancers. This was an unusual finding, since rats rarely were afflicted with stomach tumors. Therefore, Fibiger decided to learn why the three rats had developed stomach cancer.

The first step in Fibiger's investigation of the cancers was to question the laboratory animal dealer from whom he had purchased the rats. Where did the dealer get the rats? The reply was that the rats came from a sugar refinery. Following up on this lead, Fibiger went to the sugar refinery with the idea that perhaps he might find there a clue to the cause of the stomach tumors in the three rats. An inspection of the refinery, however, revealed nothing unusual, other than the fact that the plant was well populated with cockroaches. At first, Fibiger dismissed the roaches. Then he had second thoughts about them and began to consider a possible link among the roaches, rats, and tumors. Roaches crawled into all kinds of places and ate all sorts of things. The roaches in the sugar refinery might be contaminated with filth or with some organism that was transferred to the rats when the rodents ate the roaches. In turn, the filth or organism might have produced the tumors in the stomachs of the rats.

Fibiger decided to test this theory. He set up a controlled

experiment in his laboratory. He collected great numbers of roaches from the sugar refinery and fed them to rats that did not come from the sugar refinery. His rats normally lived to the age of three years, and he fed the roaches to them for the entire life spans of the rodents. When a rat died, he conducted an autopsy. And in many of the rats, he found stomach tumors.

Microscopic examinations of the rat tumors revealed an unusual situation. In each case, a tumor had formed around a parasite that had infested the stomachs of the deceased rats. The parasite proved to be a worm. Fibiger concluded that the larvae of the worms were carried into the rats by the roaches which the rodents had eaten. Once inside the rats, the larvae entered the muscles. From here, they migrated to the stomachs of the rats, where they developed into adults, attaching themselves to the stomach walls. This discovery excited Fibiger, for it could be the answer as to why the rats had developed stomach tumors. What he had done with his rat-and-roaches experiment was to produce—for the first time in cancer research—an artificial tumor in a laboratory animal.

Fibiger's discovery was pounced on by some of Maud's opponents. They claimed that Fibiger's experiments disputed Maud's contention that heredity played a major role in the transmission of cancer. Their claims were strengthened when Fibiger was able to produce a cancer in his rats almost whenever he wished. Here was proof that cancer was not inherited. Fibiger received accolades from the scientific community for his discovery. He had opened up a whole new line of investigation into the cause of cancer. And for his work, he received the Nobel Prize for physiology and medicine in 1926.

Other scientists, encouraged by Fibiger's discovery, started cancer-research projects. Most of them tried to produce artificial cancers by methods other than that employed by Fibiger, and in different animals. Fibiger himself tried to produce worm-related tumors in other species of animals, but without success. Three investigators at the Institute for Cancer Research at Columbia University in New York City conducted experiments along the lines of those pursued by Fibiger. By using Fibiger's techniques, the Columbia researchers succeeded in producing cancerous tumors in the livers of rats by feeding the rodents the larvae of the common tapeworm, *Taenia taeniaeformis*. The tapeworms had been found in some laboratory cats. Eventually, malignant tumors appeared in the livers of some rats that had ingested tapeworms.

Maud Slye's critics quickly pointed out, some gleefully, others triumphantly, that the results of the Columbia experiments demonstrated that cancer was not a hereditary disease. But their glee and triumph were short-lived, for the Columbia researchers themselves stated that although the tapeworm eggs were instrumental in producing malignant tumors in rat livers, the rats so afflicted showed strong differences as far as their family or strain was concerned. The researchers added that this finding was in line with the observations of Maud Slye on the occurrence of spontaneous tumors in her laboratory mice. Also, some rats in the Columbia experiments, stated the researchers, developed tumors in other organs, such as the breasts, instead of in the liver. This showed that there was no connection between the irritation and infection caused by the tapeworms and the incidence of cancer.

When Maud read the report on the Columbia experiments, she commented that the rats developed in time the cancers to which they were hereditarily predisposed. The tumors produced in the rats appeared only in *susceptible* individuals from *susceptible* strains of *susceptible* rats. This experiment, said Maud, emphasized what she had been saying all along: inheritance was a factor in the incidence of cancer. As for the irritation factor, which existed with the introduction of the tapeworm eggs and later by the adult worms, both hereditary predisposition and irritation were necessary to produce the tumors. This was true for the Columbia experiments and for others in which a source of irritation was introduced.

Some scientists regarded Maud's statement about irritation and hereditary predisposition both being necessary to produce cancer as a backing off from her original stand on the cause of cancer — that is, that inheritance was the sole factor in the incidence of cancer. But Maud denied any change in her conclusions, stating that her stand was still the same, and that she had never said inheritance was the only factor in the causation of cancer.

The irritation theory of cancer started a series of experiments in different parts of the world. Two Japanese researchers decided to test the relationship of tar and cancer. Some scientists believed that coal tar was a cause of cancer, particularly when it was discovered that workers in the coal-tar industry developed warts that ultimately became cancerous. In their irritation experiments, the two Japanese researchers painted the ears of rabbits with tar at various intervals. In time, they witnessed the appearance of tumorous growths on the ears painted with tar. Next, the tumors were removed from the rabbit ears and then transplanted into normal rabbits. The transplants were successful and the rabbits that had received the transplanted tumors became cancerous. This experiment caused considerable excitement among cancer researchers. The Japanese researchers had demonstrated another kind of artificially induced cancer that could be observed and examined under controlled laboratory conditions. The reaction of scientists familiar with and critical of Maud Slye's work was: "How about that, Maud Slye?" Her answer was simply that the rabbits developing the original cancers and the artificially induced cancers already had a hereditary predisposition to cancer.

Many scientists saw the Japanese experiments as a major breakthrough in cancer research and possibly cancer control. Consequently, a large number of experiments were conducted on the relationship between tar and cancer. Several English researchers learned that by using synthesized coal-tar products, they could produce cancers in laboratory mice. Then a snag appeared in the tar-and-cancer experiments. Some researchers found that although they could easily produce cancers in mice and rabbits by tar irritation, it was not so easy to produce it in rats.

Actually, the tar experiments did not bring forth any evidence to disprove Maud's contention that inheritance played a major role in the incidence of cancer. If anything, the tar experiments more or less confirmed what she had been saying: irritation, whether produced by tar or by anything else, was one of the necessary factors in cancer incidence. The other necessary factor was a hereditary predisposition to cancer, as Maud Slye's mice had displayed over a long period of time. Given the hereditary predisposition, a stimulus such as irritation could produce tumors. Yet Maud had also demonstrated that many mice that were subjected to irritation did not develop cancer.

What the tar experiments did demonstrate was that coal tar and products made from it were carcinogens, or substances that could cause cancer.

Maud weathered the coal-tar crisis without too much difficulty. Then another tumor research project that threatened her theory was resurrected. In 1909, Francis Peyton Rous, a New York pathologist, noticed that a chicken in his laboratory (a Plymouth Rock hen) had developed a tumor on its right breast. The tumor aroused Rous's curiosity, and he decided to learn more about it. First, he anesthetized the hen and removed most of the tumor. Next, he inoculated small pieces of the tumor into the left breast and abdomen of another hen. He duplicated the procedure with two other hens, both of which had been hatched from the same setting of eggs as the hen that originally developed the breast tumor.

A little more than a month after Rous inoculated the hens

with the tumor tissue, the hen that first developed the breast tumor died from cancer of the peritoneal cavity. One of the other hens that had been inoculated with tumor tissue from the first hen eventually developed a large tumor. Rous had artificially produced a tumor. His experiment with the Plymouth Rock hens was the first in which a bird tumor had been successfully transplanted into birds. The tumor transplanted by Rous, which became known as Rous Tumor Number 1, soon became an important laboratory tool for cancer researchers. All of the growths produced by Rous's methods of inoculation were very virulent tumors. Tiny bits of the tumor were carried by the blood into lungs and other tissues of the birds that received the transplants.

Naturally, Rous's transplant experiments caused a stir among cancer researchers, and not only because he had shown that certain fowl tumors could be transmitted by grafting tumor cells. He had also demonstrated that he could obtain from chicken tumors a solution that would pass through a fine filter without losing its potency. Rous's tumor experiments had some other interesting aspects. For example, even when it was passed through a fine filter, the solution showed no traces of any organisms, yet it was able to produce tumors in chickens. Rous also showed that the solution could be frozen and thawed many times without losing its virulency. What was even more astonishing was that Rous could withdraw some solution from a tumor on a chicken, inject it into the breast muscle of another chicken, and produce a tumor at the same site as that at which the original tumor occurred on the first chicken. Through his experiments, Rous was the first researcher to propose the virus theory of cancer causation. He won the Nobel Prize in Physiology and Medicine in 1966.

The action and potency of Rous Tumor Number 1 was investigated by two British scientists, a microscopist and a pathologist. What they did was to separate the supposed cancer-producing solution into two portions. They claimed that one portion was a chemical, the other was a true virus capable of producing cancerous tumors in fowl. The two scientists found that they could cultivate viruses in the virus portion of the solution. Yet, when only the virus portion was injected into a chicken, no tumors were produced. Only when the two portions of the solution were injected together was it possible to produce tumors.

William Gye, the pathologist of this British team of researchers, claimed that the chemical portion of the tumor solution could be extracted from all human cancers. He also stated that the virus portion of a tumor solution could be isolated from other sources of cancer; for example, from cancerous tumors in mice, as well as from chicken and human cancers. Although these two researchers managed to produce some tumorous growths by injecting the tumor solution, their experiments were not conclusive. Other pathologists did not accept their conclusions. Their work was further downgraded when other researchers were unable to produce any tumors when they duplicated the methods and procedures of the two British scientists. Most pathologists thought that the two British researchers probably did produce growths, but the growths were not cancers. Most important for Maud Slye, the British experiments in no way diminished her experiments and conclusions on the inheritability of cancer.

THREE

"In this laboratory," Maud Slye frequently told her visitors, "only the mice are kings. All others are secondary."

She meant every word of it. Her mice were the most important creatures in her laboratory. Without them, she never could have started her cancer-research project. When she began her study of nervous disarrangement in her Japanese waltzing mice, the common mouse, *Mus musculus,* was the most valuable laboratory animal known to research scientists. This mouse was an ideal animal for medical research, mainly because of its ability to adapt to all kinds of laboratory conditions. More important for Maud Slye and other cancer researchers, the mouse came closest to human beings in the percentages of individuals that developed cancer and in the types and locations of the tumors.

The mouse had been associated with human beings for many centuries and was believed to have evolved in the grain-producing regions of Asia. From their place of origin, mice spread to all parts of the world, moving with migrating or traveling human beings on ships and other kinds of conveyances. Mice were condemned as pests, stealers of grain, and carriers of disease. As such, they were proscribed and eradicated whenever and wherever they were found. Few people had any consideration for them. Therefore, the acceptance of the mouse as a pet and research animal was slow in coming.

Not until the nineteenth century did the mouse enter the research laboratory. *Mus musculus* turned out to be a valuable research animal, one that could be used in all kinds of experiments and studies that ranged from genetics to zoology. Some European zoologists bred mice to be used in investigating the variety of characters, such as coat colors, that might be obtained by selective breeding. Other scientists used mice to interpret the results of Galton's Law of Inheritance. Sir Francis Galton, British anthropologist, had advanced the theory that each parent contributed one quarter of the total heritage of an offspring, that each grandparent contributed one sixteenth of the total heritage, and so on in a rapidly diminishing percentage. Galton's law indicated that a hereditary character had little chance of reappearing after a lapse of generations.

Mice, because of their high reproductive rate, proved to be the most practical laboratory animals to test Galton's Law of Inheritance. However, the data obtained from these early mouse-breeding experiments were not interpreted correctly at the time. And much of this early genetic work was set aside to lie fallow, to be revived only when there was a resurrection of Gregor Mendel's heredity experiments on plants.

In 1907, Clarence Cook Little, a student at Harvard University who was later to become Maud Slye's chief competitor and critic in the field of cancer research, began studying the inheritance of coat color in mice. Little conducted his experiments under the guidance of William E. Castle, an eminent geneticist. A pair of mice known to carry the recessive genes for diluting coat color formed the basic stock for Little's experiments. In the next few years, he bred the descendents of this pair of mice, mating brother to sister, for more than twenty generations. Little was very careful to use only healthy, vigorous mice in his mating program. As a result of this mouse-breeding program, Little produced the first inbred strain of laboratory mice, which he named "bdr." Later, the name was changed to DBA, after the three recessive genes in the strain: dilution, brown, and nonagouti.

Subsequently, other strains of mice were produced by mouse breeders or fanciers for use in laboratories. A number of laboratories conducted their own mouse-breeding programs, developing various strains for specialized research.

Many of the mouse strains were developed for use in cancer research. Cancer researchers and others soon learned that these little animals, formerly considered pests, could make a significant contribution to medical research. Laboratory mice represented biological materials that scientists could use in studies and experiments with confidence. The mice were not only adaptable to laboratory conditions, they could also be adapted to a wide variety of experiments and tests. For one thing, researchers could control the variables in their biological materials, the mice, and could include only those factors they wanted in their experimental plans. The thinking was that when there was a great deal of uniformity among a colony of laboratory mice, fewer mice would be needed to achieve a desired standard of accuracy or repetition in a particular experiment. Maud Slye knew this; so did other cancer researchers.

But Maud Slye regarded her mice as more than mere biological materials for research. She treated them as living creatures that were capable of feeling pain and as animals that responded to attention and care. Maud gave the mice a great deal of attention and expert care. This was not a pose on her part or an assumed attitude to ward off the violent criticism and emotional condemnation of the use of animals in medical research voiced by the militant antivivisectionists of the period. Maud had a genuine regard for her mice. After all, she fed them, treated their battle wounds and diseases, and, when they died, tried to learn the cause of their deaths. The mice were her whole life, and their destinies were inexorably intertwined with hers. Mice were indeed kings in Maud's laboratory, and they lived in a kind of mouse Utopia, a paradise in which no mouse was subjected to cruelty or neglect.

One of the factors that helped to make Maud's laboratory a mouse Utopia was their freedom from the dangers that wild mice had to face every day. There were no prowling cats, eager and ready to pounce on an unwary mouse. There were no hawks, owls, weasels, or other predators lurking behind cages or doors, waiting for some careless mouse to wander within range of jaws or talons. Equally important for the well-being of the mice, they had no need to hunt for food. Maud saw to it that each mouse received a proper diet and an adequate ration. In the beginning, she went without food herself so that her mice would not be deprived of food. Later, when she became a member of the Sprague Memorial Institute staff and was given a salary, sho no longer had to skip meals in order to provide food for her constantly growing mouse colony.

Maud's mice lived in relative peace and contentment, and even the most critical visitor to the laboratory had to admit that if ever a mouse had found its rodent heaven, it was in Maud Slye's laboratory. Yet a kind of sword of Damocles hung over some of the mice. It was cancer. The diseases that often killed off mice in other laboratories—mouse pox, spontaneous encephalitis, pneumonia, salmonellosis, pasteurellosis, and infantile diarrhea—were not present in Maud's laboratory. She eliminated the tendency to mouse diseases by selective breeding. By doing so, she established an important fact: by the use of selective breeding, it was possible to eliminate certain animal diseases. She also demonstrated that selective breeding programs could greatly increase the life span of the mice. Many mice in her laboratory lived to be two and three years of age, a life span that was not equaled by the average wild mouse.

The elimination of mouse diseases was not merely a side effect or extra benefit from Maud's cancer research. It was vital to her investigations into the inheritability of cancer. In a laboratory geared for research that might eventually help to prevent or control cancer, it was imperative to prevent all other kinds of diseases. Only then could the researcher know that he or she had truly prevented cancer. Cancer in human beings, Maud stated, was a disease of middle age and later life. Since other diseases could not be prevented in human beings, it was difficult to know whether or not a particular person would have died from cancer had he or she lived long enough. Because of this knowledge, Maud spared no effort in keeping her mice alive and free from disease for the longest period of time possible.

Maud could not resist talking about her mice to visitors. She would pick up a mouse and cup it in her hands so that the animal would not fall and injure itself. She would then describe the life history of the mouse, informing the visitor whether it was cancerous or noncancerous, or a mouse that was presently free from cancer, although there was cancer in its ancestry. She would point to hundreds of mice busily eating, the sound of their steady gnawing filling the room. "Life in this little world of mice is happy and content," she would say. "The mothers bear their babies without difficulty or pain. They nurse the babies faithfully and bring them up to adolescence strong and vigorous."

For those visitors who had more than a passing interest in the Mouse Lady and her mice, there was plenty of evidence to substantiate what Maud told them. All they had to do was look around at the thousands of mice in their comfortable cages. The mice themselves were documentation enough.

Maud was too honest to deny that there were times when all was not harmonious among the mice. All animals fight among themselves, and intraspecies strife is not a rarity with laboratory animals. Maud's mice were no exception. There were "personal quarrels among the males," as Maud explained it, "and with which I have nothing to do." Males sometimes fought with males, and females with females. Every research laboratory keeping mice has the same problem. It is all part of animal behavior and is one of the risks of keeping mice, especially males, in the same cage. Though the obvious solution would be to separate combative males, it is not always possible.

Mice do not have a high social organization, even though they may live in close proximity to each other, as in a communal cage or pen in a laboratory. Yet they show a discernible pattern of social behavior, and it is exhibited by fighting, mating, and care of the young. Females also fight, but it is the battles between males that often have disastrous results. When two males lock together in battle, they usually end up with severe wounds. Sometimes a fight may end with the death of one of the contestants. There is also the possibility of a peculiar finale to a fight between males: the victor castrates the vanquished mouse.

Maud often observed the aggressive behavior of her male mice. First, the two antagonists would stare fixedly at each other, as though each were trying to intimidate or stare down the other. When intimidation failed, the two mice would engage in a series of actions that included dancing, nosing each other around the cage, kicking and pawing, wrestling, chasing each other, and finally a gesture of submission by the weaker mouse. Usually, a fight was preceded by the fluffing out of the fur and a rapid tail rattling by each mouse. Once the dominance of a male was settled by a battle, peace and order returned to the group. However, when Maud introduced a strange male into the cage, another fight took place to establish dominance. What was interesting was that the winner of a fight between males was not always the number-one mouse when it came to mating with females. This was a departure from other species, such as grazing animals, where the victor in a fight between males has the right to copulate with the females first.

Although Maud's primary concern in breeding mice and maintaining a colony was to find a link between cancer and heredity, she could not avoid learning a great deal about mouse behavior. Her contact with the mice day after day and month after month, her constant observation of each mouse, and the routine work involved in the physical care of the mouse colony gave her an expertise in mouse behavior and husbandry. How a mouse reacted or behaved during the course of a disease, such as cancer, was important to Maud. Just as human beings had their behavior altered or affected by a disease, so did Maud's mice. Any change in the behavior of her mice, whether it was caused by cancer or some other stimuli, was dutifully recorded on a chart, both from the standpoint of scientific research and from Maud's concern for the welfare of her mice.

Maud's protectiveness for her mice often bordered on the over-anxious side, like that of a responsible mother for the safety and welfare of her children. One of Maud's constant fears was that something would happen to them, some catastrophe. She hated to leave the mice unattended.

However, her endurance had a limit. She could not be with the mice every hour of the day. There were times, few, to be sure, when she attended a meeting or was asked to lecture in another city. These were the times when she became anxious about her mice. To help solve the problem, she arranged for a young student at the university to act as a kind of watchman in the mouse laboratory at night. The young man took some of the load from Maud's shoulders, but like a fussy mother, she often came to the laboratory late at night to check up on the mice.

One winter evening Maud was awakened by a howling blizzard, the kind that often strikes Chicago, which blew down across Lake Michigan from Canada, bringing cold arctic air and snow. She lay awake, listening to the roaring and swelling of the wind and to the sound of the sleet pounding against her bedroom window. She felt safe in her room, knowing that the full fury of the storm could not touch her.

Then she thought about her mice. Were they all right? Had she left any windows open in the laboratory? And if she had, would the student watchman close them to shut out the icy blast of the blizzard?

Thinking about the mice became a torture to her. Unable to stand the suspense any longer, she got out of bed, dressed quickly, and went out into the blizzard. She had to push herself against the wind and shield her face from the stinging ice particles that hurtled at her out of the darkness. She managed to reach the laboratory without slipping or falling. She hurried inside, turning on the lights and rushing to the mouse sections. The rooms were warm and dry. No windows were open. All of her mice were safe. She heard them gnawing, and it was a pleasant sound that banished all of her fears. After a tour around the building, she put out the lights and went out into the storm again, but this time with a lighter heart.

Maud continued to be apprehensive about her mice. If anything should happen to them—if the building should catch fire and her mice be destroyed—she would lose not only years of work, but thousands of friends. Few people at the university and in the scientific world were aware of Maud's deep concern about her mice. To them, she was a cold, reserved scientist, a laboratory researcher to whom mice and other animals were simply a means to a discovery or a conclusion. They envisioned her as a female scientist in a white coat, working long hours in her laboratory, peering into a microscope at mouse tissue, or coolly dissecting a dead mouse on the autopsy table. Maud did create this impression of the competent, detached scientist. But it was just that, an impression.

Perhaps that was the way she wanted to show herself, hiding her true self and her feelings about her mice and life and science behind the calm mask of the research scientist. She reserved her real feelings and dreams for those moments when she was in her garden or listening to music or writing poetry. Her sensitivity would not permit her to expose her inner self to the scrutiny or scalpels of her scientific colleagues, who were always eager to find a flaw or weakness in this gifted woman. Therefore, she sought safety from their personal cuts and slashes and confided only in her mice or a singing bird or a white flower in her garden.

As Maud continued to breed her cancerous and noncancerous mice and to accumulate data to support her contention that cancer was an inheritable disease, she became more vulnerable to critical attacks by other scientists. There were a number of cancer researchers who, because of professional jealousy or for other reasons, were waiting for a chance to discredit her and her work. Any emotionalism Maud displayed toward her mice would, if brought to the attention of her would-be detractors, cause her considerable embarrassment and a good deal of difficulty. Her maternal concern for the mice would be seized on as an example of femininity and held up to view as an example of unscientific behavior. Maud walked a tightrope in the scientific community because she was a woman.

Thus Maud hid her true feelings from the scientific world. What concern she showed for her mice many scientists attributed to her fear that if anything happened to them, a lifetime of work would be wiped out. This was the prevalent attitude when Maud decided to take her mice with her when she had to go to the sickbed of her aged mother in California. The nature of her mother's illness was such that Maud would have to be away from the laboratory for a fairly long time. Rather than risk losing the mice and her records to some disaster while she was away, she opted to take the mice and valuable data with her. This decision meant that she would have to transport several thousand mice, as well as boxes of papers, to California. She solved the problem by renting a boxcar into which she loaded the mice and records. University people exchanged glances and grins when Maud took her precious mice to California, but the researchers among them thought they understood why she did it. Most of them could think of no greater calamity than losing the fruits of their own research, and they felt that the Mouse Lady was wise to cart her mice and records along with her.

Though Maud took pains to hide her affection for her mice from most people, particularly scientists, some people were privileged to see her display tenderness toward a mouse. These were usually close friends or relatives who came to the mouse laboratory, or "City of Mice," as some people referred to it, on a visit. When she felt at ease with a person, Maud would carefully pick up a mouse and soothe the animal with soft talk, so that it would stop struggling and lie still in her cupped hands. She knew each mouse as an individual.

"Here is a little mouse whose history I know by heart," she would tell a visitor. "See that lump under his neck? That is a thyroid cancer. This mouse is the twenty-eighth generation of mouse family number JD 306268." Then she would smile at the puzzled look on the visitor's face and explain, "We number our mouse families the way names are given to human families."

For the visitor who was really interested, Maud would provide more information about a particular mouse or family. She would explain that the ancestors of a certain mouse had a particular kind of cancer, and that 133 members of the family had died from cancer. She would point out that the mouse's grandmother died from cancer, but that his father and mother had not. Then she would tell the visitor that cancer skips generations, only to recur later on.

She would lead a visitor to a cage in which a mouse was sleeping. Huddled nearby in a nest hollowed out of shredded newspaper would be some baby mice. "Here," Maud would say, "are a mother mouse and her healthy babies. The mother is taking her noonday nap. Both she and her babies are free from cancer. I have kept track of her family tree, which includes more than 200 mice. None of them had cancer." When she finished talking about the mother mouse and her babies, Maud would move quietly away from the sleeping mouse family, cautioning the visitor to do likewise. "We don't want to disturb their nap," she would say.

Then, at the end of her long day in the laboratory, she would make a final inspection tour of the rows and tiers of mouse cages. She would carefully check each cage to see that there was adequate food and sufficient water. She would make certain that every mouse was settled for the night. With a final look around the mouse rooms, she would leave the laboratory for the night, quietly closing the doors so as not to startle the mice and make her way across the street to her home. At bedtime, she would lie awake for a while, thinking of a poem she wanted to write:

> At night my laboratory stands
> Sheltered in dark, all its wide work of day
> Silenced for rest. On both its sides
> Flanked by still space, it looms alone
> The sky above it and the dark around.
> Oh, all my heart is there!
> I watch it standing in the night
> And silent dark. . . .

FOUR

Gradually, the mouse laboratory on Drexel Avenue in Chicago gained more attention from the scientific community and from sections of the lay public. The work Maud Slye was doing, although highly controversial, was of more than passing interest to most people. Cancer was a word that brought fear to everyone. Any information that would bring even slight encouragement as to the cause and eventual control of this dreaded disease was seized by scientists, physicians, and even the press. Maud Slye's mice continued to produce valuable data on cancer and heredity, although her research and conclusions were still questioned by scientists and particularly by members of the American Society for Cancer Research. Regardless of the skepticism and criticism of her work, Maud's findings represented, so far, a most important contribution to cancer research.

With her mouse-breeding program, emphasizing proper matings, Maud was successful in eliminating cancer from mouse families in which the disease had been prevalent. Similarly, she bred cancer into mouse families where it had not been present. She did this by selective breeding. She found that the tendency of mice to be susceptible or resistant to cancer was definitely a hereditary characteristic. She was able to demonstrate that the offspring of two mouse parents would be completely free from cancer if the families of both parents were cancer-free. If one parent had cancer and the other was entirely free from the disease, the immediate off-spring would be cancer-free, *but they in turn could transmit cancer susceptibility to some of their offspring.* This was in accordance with Mendel's first law of heredity.

Each inherited trait is determined by two hereditary units called *alleles,* which are part of the *gene.* Alleles are transmitted in the parents' reproductive cells, or *gametes.* An individual is called *homozygous* if the two alleles are the same, and *heterozygous* if they are different. A heterozygous plant or animal is called a hybrid. In hybrids, one of the two alleles will suppress the other—it is *dominant,* whereas the other is *recessive.* Scientists identify the dominant factor by capital letters, such as AA, and the recessive factor by small letters, such as aa. The following charts show the different combinations in the alleles of the offspring when two purebred individuals are mated, when two hybrids are mated, and when one purebred parent is crossed with a hybrid.

female \ male	A	A
A	AA	AA
A	AA	AA

AA X AA =
100% AA progeny
(homozygous
dominant)

female \ male	A	A
A	AA	AA
a	Aa	Aa

AA × Aa =
50% AA progeny
(homozygous
dominant)
50% Aa progeny
(heterozygous)

female \ male	A	a
A	AA	Aa
a	Aa	aa

Aa × Aa =
50% Aa progeny
(heterozygous)
25% AA progeny
(homozygous
dominant)
25% aa progeny
(homozygous
recessive)

One of the chief criticisms leveled at Maud's conclusions was that her findings pertained only to cancer in mice. There was no evidence to relate them to cancer in human beings. But Maud insisted that her observations on mice paralleled those made on human beings. At the time, cancer caused the death of about 10 percent of the human population that reached cancer age. When the almost uniformly hybrid matings that took place among human beings were considered, argued Maud, it was apparent that the incidence of cancer was close to the expectation for a simple Mendelian character.

Since noncancerous parents could produce cancerous offspring, the parents had to be considered hybrids, that is, progeny of parents of whom one was cancerous and one was purebreeding noncancerous, or who had both (or at least one of them) been hybrids. Maud therefore concluded that the susceptibility to cancer was a recessive trait and that resistance to cancer was a dominant trait. "The fact that the cancer tendency is recessive to the normal tendency," she said, "is most encouraging, for it means that cancer can be eliminated in two generations by the right selection in mating. It also means that large numbers of individuals are by inheritance *exempt* from the probability of cancer."

These were revolutionary and challenging words. When Maud presented to the members of the American Society for Cancer Research her belief, based on her research, that the susceptibility to cancer was due to a Mendelian recessive character, their reaction was swift and denunciatory. There was a large group of fundamentalists in the membership of the Cancer Society, some of whom still leaned toward the theory that cancer was caused by a parasite, probably a virus, such as the one isolated by Rous in his chickens. They refused to accept Maud's conclusions. Some of these opponents were scientists who were also engaged in cancer research; others were scientists who simply resented the attention being given to the work of Maud Slye, particularly when, in their opinion, she had not proved her theory.

Clarence Cook Little, the researcher who had developed the

first strain of inbred mice at Harvard University, took issue with Maud's findings and conclusions. Little, now a researcher investigating the various factors in mammalian genetics and cancer, hoped to find the cause of cancer, and was engaged in the same line of research as Maud Slye. Since he wanted to be the first to discover the cause of cancer, it was only natural that he would be highly critical of the work of others, particularly when it paralleled his own research.

In her early mouse-breeding experiments, Maud had mated a gray mouse with an albino mouse, and in her report on this crossbreeding experiment, she used the terms "dominant" and "recessive." The results Maud obtained from this experiment were, according to Little, at variance with the generally accepted principles of Mendelian inheritance and incompatible with those of other researchers. Little felt that in view of the discrepancies in results, Maud should present all of her data on the inheritance of albinism in mice. He stressed the fact that a careful repetition of Maud's experiment by other researchers would be necessary before her claims could be accepted, at least by him.

Little wrote to Maud asking her if she had not made an error in her methods or conclusion. She assured him she had not. Little, in a short article in *Science*, cautioned readers of Maud's report about accepting her work:

> To those unfamiliar with the work of the geneticists, Slye's paper might be taken as presenting the well-known principle of Mendelian inheritance. With a knowledge of the facts, however, it is obvious that the type of inheritance which she outlines has not been observed in similar material by any of the [previous] investigators. That this discrepancy is not based on an oversight on the part of Miss Slye has been determined by personal correspondence.

Little followed his first article on the gray-albino mouse-breeding project with another that was published in *Science*.

First, he acknowledged that Maud had conducted a laborious experiment. Then he said, "The importance of the subject, however, is such that it is essential to understand the exact distinction between the gathering of valuable data and the interpretation of such data when gathered." He went on to say that Maud had taken advantage of a Mendelian law of heredity to study the transmission or inheritability of cancer in mice.

Maud's studies showed that the appearance and numerical value of the albino character could be predicted with certainty from the manner of mating the parents. The same was true of the whirling character of the Japanese waltzing mouse, and also of cancer, according to Maud's experiments.

Not so, declared Little. And he called on Maud to publish all of her data, pointing out "that when one investigator suggests a revolutionary hypothesis which is contrary to the experimental results obtained by a large number of investigators in the same field, it is customary to present with the hypothesis the data on which it depends for its support." However, he did admit that Maud was right when she said, in speaking about heredity, that "exceptions to what was the canon have become so numerous as to be part of the rule." Nevertheless, he requested that Maud publish the complete data on which the type of inheritance reported by her rested.

Little's criticism of Maud's experiment on albinism in mice served to cast some doubt on her cancer research. Other researchers began to snipe at her and to question her methods and conclusions. Skepticism and demands for proof and complete data were to be expected in the case of so serious and puzzling a disease as cancer. Any researcher who claimed to have discovered even a hint as to the cause of cancer was bound to have his or her work thoroughly scrutinized for possible errors in method and judgment.

Maud, of course, accepted this; what disturbed her was the vehemence with which some critics attacked her work. She could not help but feel that something more than a professional challenge was involved in the attacks. Her work seemed to be challenged on a dual basis: first, as the work of a researcher investigating a highly controversial subject and, second, as the work of a woman. All she wanted, however, was that her work be judged solely on its merits. But perhaps that was too much to ask of a scientific discipline dominated by men.

Maud found it increasingly difficult to convince other scientists of the relationship between cancer and inheritance. The problem she faced was in making known the facts of heredity and placing them in their proper relationship to other biological data. This was vital for establishing the exact value of heredity among biological influences, so that other investigators would have a firm base for future study. Maud believed that such a measure was necessary to prevent researchers from covering the same ground. Nowhere was this more important than in the effort to establish a relationship between cancer and heredity.

A large stumbling block stood in Maud's path, and that was the preconceived ideas and prejudices of fundamentalists. Oddly enough, these prejudices were not based on scientific research, but on general impressions, hearsay evidence, and the like, and they were handed down by one scientist to another, much in the manner that a craftsman may hand down his preconceived ideas and prejudices to another craftsman. In time, these preconceived ideas, prejudices, general impressions, and hearsay evidence became well-established general opinions.

Maud also had to cope with the misuse and misunderstanding of scientific terms. She was not so much concerned with this problem as it existed among lay persons as among scientists. After all, the public could not be expected to understand or properly use highly technical or scientific terms. But scientists should be able to understand and correctly use their own technical terms. In Maud's opinion, the misuse and misunderstanding of scientific terms helped to perpetuate prejudice and preconceived ideas.

One scientific term that Maud thought was misunderstood and misapplied was *eugenics*. Scientists often used the term to mean anything from personal and social hygiene, childbirth conditions, prenatal and postnatal, right on up to the facts of heredity. Eugenics, as Maud saw it, was the science that dealt with the improvement of races and breeds, especially the human race, through the control of hereditary factors. The important point to remember, stated Maud, was that eugenics was concerned with the study of human heredity.

The widely divergent uses of the term eugenics led to widespread confusion. Too many scientists were confusing the true meaning of the term with terms that were related to sanitation and congenital conditions. Maud agreed that personal and social hygiene had much to do with a good birth. They also determined those conditions that were congenital; that is, personal and social hygiene affected conditions before or at birth. But they did not in any way determine hereditary characters. True, they might influence the extent to which hereditary characters could develop, just as conditions of wholly external origin—for example, a lack of food and sunshine—could determine after birth just how far certain hereditary characters could develop.

Another term misused and misunderstood by clinicians and researchers, and with which Maud had to contend in explaining her work, was the term *congenital* when applied to diseases. Congenital was often used to mean hereditary, and vica versa. Actually, a congenital disease was one that was contracted while the fetus was still in the womb. This was not the case with a hereditary disease, which was the result of characters derived from ancestral germ plasm, inherent in the ovum and in the sperm cell. Maud maintained that by the right line of experimentation, hereditary diseases could be proved not to have been contracted while a fetus was still in the womb.

Maud was invited to speak to the members of the American Society for Cancer Research at a meeting held in Albany, New York. She took this opportunity to discuss the terminology problem, particularly as it related to cancer research and specifically as it related to her work. She told the audience that conditions or influences within the womb determined what would be congenital. Such conditions or influences would not determine characters that were hereditary, since these characters were laid down by the germ plasm and could be carried through many generations before emergence. She reminded the assembled scientists that such hereditary recessive characters as the tendency to albinism, the tendency to cancer, and the tendency to the dancing habit, as shown in the Japanese waltzing mice, had been repeatedly suppressed in mice in her laboratory for twenty-five generations.

Those twenty-five generations of mice, upon each of which Maud had kept careful records, were the evidence of what she was trying to establish about cancer and inheritance. Cancer, albinism, and the waltzing habit were, according to her experiments, submerged beneath a dominant character; that is they were carried along through generation after generation of hybrid mice showing the dominant character. But these dormant tendencies were always a potential in the strain of mice, as long as she bred hybrid carriers that had the recessive trait. When she eventually bred two of these hybrid carriers, the recessive character would emerge in one quarter of the offspring, although the cancer, albinism, or the waltzing habit had been submerged in hybrid carriers for many generations.

From time to time, as Maud lectured them, various members of the male-dominated audience would exchange glances or raise eyebrows at some point she made. But they listened attentively as she went on with her lecture.

Such behavior of any character, [continued Maud] took it entirely out of the realm of the congenital. Instead, the behavior placed it among the characters that were indisputably hereditary. The test of whether or not a character could be transmitted through generation after generation without its frank emergence should always be made in the study of the inheritability of any recessive character. This was necessary to ascertain that it is truly hereditary and not congenital.

Despite the apparent interest in the possible inheritability of diseases on the part of many biologists and physicians, they had conducted very few studies to relate heredity to disease. That was why Maud's research was so important. She was attempting to find the relationship between heredity and disease. Yet even though there was a dearth of data on the subject, a number of scientists held an opinion, often a strong one, whenever the subject of linking a specific disease with heredity arose. Thus, they put forth the opinions when there was no basis for them. Some scientists argued that there was no hereditary basis for diseases. Others exhibited a readiness to accept the opinion that any given disease was not hereditary when they had inadequate data to support such an opinion. "Unfortunately," said Maud Slye, "even when there was incontrovertible evidence that a disease was hereditary, it made no impression on some scientists."

Perhaps one of the most serious obstacles Maud faced in establishing the facts and influences of heredity in her mouse-breeding program was the general misconception of the nature of heredity itself. There was also a misunderstanding among scientists of the type of experiment that was needed to prove the inheritability or noninheritability of any disease. A fundamental view of the times was that if an investigator studied two parents, such a study was adequate. But Maud's experience with her mice showed this view to be erroneous. An investigator had to study more than the two parents of an offspring; otherwise, he or she would be unable to explain why two black parent mice could produce white babies, or two brown-eyed human parents could produce blue-eyed children, or two human or two mouse parents without cancer could produce offspring that developed cancer.

Maud admitted that it could be argued that black hair in mice and brown-eye color in human beings were not inheritable, since they did not appear in the offspring that resulted from the crossmatings she postulated. Too often, researchers decided that cancer was not hereditary on the basis that it did not appear in the offspring. The trouble was that positive conclusions regarding heredity were frequently based on data concerning only the parents. This was wrong. Also, too many scientists announced the inheritability of a disease on so inconclusive a test as mating two individuals with the same disease and finding that the immediate offspring have the disease. Then there were those investigators who stopped too short; they accepted the record of only the two parents and the four grandparents. This was also wrong in Maud's experience, for it was easily possible, in heredity, that there could appear in the *third* generation a character that was not shown by either parent or any of the four grandparents.

In her mouse laboratory, Maud had demonstrated these key factors in the cancer-heredity relationship. She conducted an experiment in which she could derive albino mice by the classic method when there was no albinism in the parents or grandparents. First, pigmentation or color was dominant over the lack of pigmentation, or albinism. When Maud bred two black mice, one of which was a hybrid black; that is, it carried the potential for albinism, and the other was a purebreeding black (one that would produce only black offspring), the immediate offspring were black. However, one half of the litter would be purebreeding black mice and one half would be hybrid black mice. Nothing in the external appearance of the black mice indicated which were dominant black and which were hybrid black. If Maud accidentally selected for both parents of the next generation two hybrid black mice from such a cross, one quarter of the offspring would be albino.

Thus, she was able to demonstrate that albino mice could be obtained from ancestry that showed no white mice in either parents or grandparents. When she mated two of the white mice, she got a 100 percent albino strain. This strain remained 100 percent albino unless she introduced pigmentation into it by way of pigmented mice. By mating two recessive albino mice derived from hybrid black mice, she was able to develop a strain that, though it had apparently been 100 percent black, was now 100 percent albino, or white.

Since Maud believed cancer susceptibility to be a recessive character, she was able to obtain in the third generation some cancerous individuals from parents and grandparents that were cancer-free. Each parent was a hybrid noncancerous mouse, but in each pair of grandparents, one individual was a purebreeding noncancerous mouse and one was a hybrid noncancerous mouse. The mating of the two hybrid noncancerous mice resulted in a litter composed of one quarter cancerous young. She could then in one generation derive a 100 percent extracted cancer strain from what apparently had been a 100 percent noncancerous family.

In additional color-breeding experiments, Maud prevented, by continuous mating of purebreeding black mice with hybrid black mice, the appearance of albinism for twenty-five generations. She could theoretically do the same for fifty generations. As long as one parent in each pair of mice was a purebreeding black, no white would occur in the offspring, but albinism would be carried potentially in the strain. She could continue this for as many generations as she wished, but when, in any generation, both of the parents she selected were hybrid black, then 25 percent white, or albino, offspring would appear.

Maud found in her cancer-breeding experiments that as

long as one parent was a purebreeding cancer-resistant mouse, no cancer appeared in the offspring. However, when one parent was a hybrid cancer-resistant mouse, cancer susceptibility would inevitably be carried potentially in the family for many generations. Finally, when two hybrid cancer-resistant mice were mated, one quarter of their immediate offspring were cancer susceptible.

Maud believed that in the chance matings of human beings, the mating of two hybrid carrier individuals of any given recessive character was almost certain to take place sooner or later. When it did occur, the recessive character would show up in about 25 percent of the children. This accounted for the sudden appearance of cancer in families in which the disease had not been known for more than two generations.

Maud constantly explained these basic principles of heredity in her mouse-breeding program as it related to her research on the inheritability of cancer. When these facts or principles were understood, she kept telling scientists and physicians who doubted her work, the absurdity of trying to settle the question by the statistical method advocated by the biometricians would at once be apparent. Though the statistician, in attempting to settle the question of the inheritability of cancer (or any other disease), could perhaps get the facts on the life and death of two parents, and possibly that of the four grandparents, he could not learn which of these ancestors had been a purebreeding cancer-resistant individual and which a hybrid cancer-resistant individual. There was no way to discover these facts except by the experimental method of selective breeding and analysis with the right number and kind of hybrid crosses. Only by the experimental method, declared Maud, could the question of the inheritability of any character whatever be settled definitely. And that was what she was trying to do in her extensive mouse-breeding project.

Some scientists accepted the heredity facts and principles outlined by Maud, although they did not accept all of her results. However, most of the fundamentalists, members of the American Society for Cancer Research, were not only unimpressed with Maud's delineation of the basic principles of heredity as they pertained to her mouse experiments, but were very critical of her work itself. They stressed the apparent disagreement between geneticists themselves as to the behavior of cancer heredity. They alluded to the fact that the inheritance behavior of grafted tumors, such as those implanted by Rous and other investigators, indicated that multiple factors were present, among which was a dominant character that determined the "take" of grafted tumors in the first hybrid generation. Yet, said some of the fundamentalists, Maud Slye insisted that cancer inheritability was due to a recessive character. What Maud said contradicted the available evidence. And because of this supposed contradiction, the fundamentalists dismissed Maud's conclusion that cancer was inheritable.

The tar-and-cancer question kept reappearing to plague Maud. Her critics constantly brought it up, mainly because they thought it was a question that would trip her up. Although framed in different ways, the question was: How did Maud explain the appearance of cancer in animals painted with a tarry brush, when she kept insisting that cancer was inherited? Most of her tormentors knew that the subject of tar and cancer was still being investigated and that much more work had to be done before any conclusions could be drawn. But they seemed to enjoy goading Maud into making statements which they hoped they could easily refute.

Maud did answer them, over and over again. "Whether or not it is eventually found that tar-cancer can be produced in all subjects, the conclusions cannot decide the question of the inheritability of cancer. The conclusions must be in agreement with all other facts of cancer, one of which is its demonstrated inheritability, as shown by the mice in my laboratory."

But her detractors were not satisfied with her answers. They refused to let her off the hook, baiting her with the fact that tar could produce cancer in experimental animals without any evidence of inheritability. Maud tartly replied that nobody could deny the inheritability of the tendency to grow hair. Yet the continued painting of tar on the skin of a mouse or rabbit destroyed the hair-growing mechanism. In all probability, Maud stated, continued painting of the skin with strong coal tar would destroy every inherited tissue and every inherited function of the body. In short, no tissue, no function, and no tendency of the body was immune from destruction. Coal tar products of sufficient concentration were very destructive agents and undoubtedly could destroy the cancer-resisting mechanism.

What was more important in Maud's opinion was that the methods used in the coal-tar experiments were destroying the very tendency they were supposed to test; to wit, inheritance factors. The question of the inheritability of cancer resistance could not be settled by determining whether cancer could or could not be experimentally produced by any given method in any given set of subjects. There was not and could not be any complete biologic control in the field of heredity in such experiments. She summed up her discussion of the tar-and-cancer question by stating that "there could be no certainty that it was only the inheritability of the tendency to cancer resistance that was being tested in such experiments."

And there the matter rested, with Maud Slye, the front-runner as far as a long and laborious investigation of cancer and inheritance was concerned, insisting that the rabbits that developed tumors from tar applications already possessed the susceptibility to cancer, and with the fundamentalists insisting that cancer was not an inheritable disease.

FIVE

Eventually some of Maud's opponents in the field of cancer research changed their arguments. They put forth the idea that since human heredity could not be presently controlled, mainly because human matings could not be controlled, the demonstrated facts of heredity, such as those produced by Maud Slye and her mice, did not apply to human beings. And since they did not apply, they should be dismissed.

Francis Carter Wood, a researcher at the Institute of Cancer Research, Columbia University, and editor of the *Journal of Cancer Research*, was one of the scientists who decided to dismiss Maud's data. In the *Journal of the American Medical Association*, Wood made the following statement:

Of course the animal experimentations done by Maud Slye in Chicago and by Bullock and Curtis in my laboratory have definitely proved that in animals a susceptibility to cancer is transmissible. Of that there can be no question. The breeding experiments, however, are so complicated and take so long that if they were applied to human beings it would mean that for the last 5000 years both parents of those unfortunate human beings who had cancer would have had to have cancer. This is a concentration of breeding which cannot occur in the human race. So the facts of the high incidence of cancer in their [Slye's and those of the researchers at Columbia] experimental studies cannot be applied in full to human beings.

71

Although the general public was not aware of the great controversy going on in the field of cancer research, especially over the work of Maud Slye, most scientists and physicians who read the various medical and research journals did know. And many of them awaited Maud's answer to Wood's statement.

They did not have long to wait, for Maud responded to Wood's article in quick time. She countered his arguments with facts obtained from her mouse experiments. First, the idea that it would take five thousand years to test the inheritability of cancer in human beings with double-cancerous parentage in each generation simply had no scientific basis. Second, and equally untenable, was the statement made by Wood that because scientists could not make a five-thousand-year test of the inheritability of human cancer, discarding the facts of cancer heredity in human beings was more or less justified.

The 100-percent cancer strains produced in Maud Slye's laboratory and in those of other cancer researchers had been obtained from a double-cancerous parentage somewhere in the particular strain of mice under study. But this did not mean that there had to be a series of double-cancerous parentages for any length of time corresponding to five thousand years of human heredity, as Wood concluded—or, Maud emphasized, for even more than one generation. "One generation of double-cancerous parentage will produce 100 percent cancer-susceptible offspring, exactly as double albino parentage for only one generation will produce 100 percent albino offspring," Maud told the doubting Thomases in the scientific community.

She explained that the long series of many generations of 100-percent-cancerous strains of mice had been carefully charted in her laboratory. They had been charted not because countless generations had been necessary to produce the strains, but because she wanted to demonstrate that they actually were 100-percent-cancerous strains of mice. These cancerous strains continued as such for as many generations as she used a double-cancerous parentage. Not only did the strains of double-cancerous parentage prove the inheritability of cancer, they also demonstrated the behavior of cancer in hybridization. That was the potent proof.

The difficulty in studying human heredity was not that scientists could not expect to have a double-cancerous parentage—or any other type of double parentage—for five thousand years, as Wood claimed, but that scientists could not obtain the exact facts for even one generation of human beings. It was because of the lack of exact data on human heredity, and because scientists could not, of course, experiment on human beings, that Maud Slye and other cancer researchers had to get their data from animal experimentation. Nevertheless, Maud said, "That we are justified in applying these facts [obtained from animal experiments], where they are basic biologic facts, is one of the best assets derived from the discovery of the fact of evolution."

It was the fundamentalist doctrine that posed the greatest obstacle for Maud Slye and other cancer researchers. Publications of the American Society for the Control of Cancer generally questioned the validity of research projects dealing with the inheritability of cancer in mice or in men. These publications helped to govern the propaganda concerning cancer heredity, which was prevalent in the various cancer-control meetings and symposia held in various sections of the United States.

Much of the cancer propaganda manufactured in the United States, which disputed the cancer-heredity theories and conclusions of Maud Slye, was often quoted abroad. Thus, Maud not only had to contend with critics and detractors at home, but also in a number of foreign countries. She complained about the rigidity of the fundamentalists and their cavalier dismissal of her data and conclusions on cancer inheritability.

"In no other fields of scientific endeavor," she told a group of physicians and scientists, "do we assume that, because at present we cannot make a particular test of a demonstrated scientific fact—such as controlling human matings—therefore it is not a fact and we can forthright discard it." And she added that conclusions drawn in higher mathematics and physics were not discarded just because they were complicated. Yet Francis Wood advocated the dismissal of her data and conclusions because they were "complicated."

A major difficulty in the study of human heredity was that the researcher could not collect accurate data extending over more than three generations, roughly his or her own lifespan. "But," said Maud, "this does not mean that there are no heredity facts unbrokenly expressing themselves in the human species, just as they do in other animals of a shorter lifespan, whose exact records are being taken." Maud urged that permanent records of periodic examinations of each living human being, as well as permanent records of accurate necropsy findings of all deceased persons, be kept.

If such records were kept, then in three generations there would be a reservoir of valuable scientific data. These data undoubtedly would include matings of double-cancerous parents, matings of double-noncancerous parents, matings of noncancerous individuals with hybrid carriers, matings of cancerous individuals with hybrid carriers, and hybrid matings. These matings would be similar to those she used to test the inheritability of cancer in her mice. One hurdle in the human matings would be that there was no way to know who was a hybrid carrier, except through the offspring. Nevertheless, until such a body of data could be obtained for the human species, similar records kept on animals, if taken accurately and correctly interpreted, would have to be the source of data for human beings.

Once again, the tar-and-cancer question bobbed up. The widespread use of tar and tar products in the United States was causing great concern, especially since cancer had been produced in laboratory animals that had been painted or daubed with tar. More researchers were achieving a high degree of success in producing tar-induced tumors on rabbits, mice, and other laboratory animals. The high percentage of growths achieved in the laboratories continued to strengthen the arguments of the fundamentalists. "Cancer is not inherited," they proclaimed in journals and from the lecture platform.

Clara Lynch, a researcher at the Rockefeller Institute, was investigating the relationship between tar and cancer. She used two strains of mice, one of which she designated as carrying a fixed high percentage of spontaneous mammary-gland cancer, 65 percent in bred females and 20 percent in unbred females. The other strain was designated as carrying a low percentage of spontaneous mammary gland cancer, 28 percent in bred females and 4 percent in unbred females. Her object was to determine if painting the skin of the mice with tar would change the incidence of cancer within the strains. She also wanted to learn if the high-percent cancer strain of mice would show a greater increase in cancers than the low-percent cancer strain.

When asked for her comments on this experiment, Maud said that Miss Lynch's method was not only the best way to test the susceptibility to skin cancer, but the only way. It would be futile to try to use anything else. But in Maud's experience, the tendency to other types and locations of neoplasms, such as mammary-gland carcinoma, had no influence on the production of spontaneous skin cancer. Moreover, Clara Lynch designated her mouse strains as having 20 and 4 percent of spontaneous cancer in unbred females, thereby carefully distinguishing between the cancer rate in bred and unbred females. Then she proceeded to use in her experiment approximately one half males, *whose susceptibility to cancer of any kind had not been expressed*. Maud further pointed out that the difference in the ages of the mice had not been accounted for or controlled in the experiment.

Maud's years of breeding cancerous and noncancerous strains of mice had taught her one important rule: that it was unscientific to assume fixed percentages of any character within a strain—as Clara Lynch had done in her tar-and-cancer experiments. The past history of cancer production within a hybrid (or heterozygous) strain could not be assumed to produce cancer within that strain in the future. She made these statements with confidence, for her mouse-breeding project was the longest and most extensive breeding program ever carried out by a single researcher.

Each of Maud's mouse strains that was producing some cancerous and some noncancerous individuals was heterozygous to cancer. She compared this to mouse strains that produced some black and some white individuals, which meant the strains were heterozygous to albinism. Every noncancerous mouse in a heterozygous cancer strain was itself heterozygous to cancer, unless at least one parent of the mouse was 100 percent noncancerous. One half of those mice that had a 100-percent noncancerous parent would be heterozygous to cancer.

Maud stated that this was true because the mating of a noncancerous mouse with a hybrid carrier produced a litter of one half noncancerous mice and one half hybrid carrier mice. Therefore, any strain of mice that yielded 4, 20, 28, or 65 percent cancer, as Clara Lynch's strains of mice were supposed to do, would be heterozygous to cancer. Also, the cancer potentiality of every one of the strain's members would depend entirely on what matings had been made, just as the strain's future cancer percentage would depend on what matings would be made. In addition to its cancerous members, such a strain of mice was made up of some homozygous noncancerous mice and some hybrid carrier mice. Nothing in the external appearance of the mice distinguished between the latter two types.

However, Maud stressed the fact that it could not be scientifically stated that any heterozygous strain of mice inherently carried a fixed percentage of cancer. All that could be said, based on her extensive experiments, was that during the life of a mouse strain, it did produce a certain percentage of cancer. She stated that with different types of mating and handling, the same strains of mice would have produced a different percentage of cancer from what she had obtained in her experiments. The point Maud was making in this discussion of cancer inheritance was that the very foundation of the tar-and-cancer experiments was weak, if not on the verge of being dismantled. The problem could never be scientifically attacked through the methods being used by the tar-and-cancer researchers.

At no time did Maud deny that tar was a factor in the growth of cancerous tumors. She recognized the necessity of stimulation, irritation, or trauma, either minute or large, as a basis for the growth of malignant tumors. The fact that various types of irritation, such as tar, play an important part in the causation of cancer in *susceptible* individuals was one of the best arguments for defining cancer as an abnormal regenerative process. The regeneration after trauma apparently was abnormal in cancer-susceptible individuals because of the lack of a differentiating mechanism in the tissues. It was this lack that was, in Maud's opinion, the hereditary element in cancer susceptibility. Or, to put it another way, the type of local response made to a given type of irritation was determined by heredity, regardless of the type of irritation.

Despite Maud's careful and patient explanation of her cancer-and-heredity theories, experiments, and conclusions, both in the scientific journals and at various meetings of physicians and scientists, there still existed a hard core of physicians and scientists who insisted that cancer was not inheritable. James Ewing of the Cornell Medical College, writing in the *Journal of Cancer Research* in 1925, discussed the work of a cancer researcher, R. Bagg. Based on the results of his experiments, Bagg concluded that 85 percent of the breast cancer that had appeared in fifteen of his mice was due entirely to his experimental procedures. Ewing wrote:

> Carcinoma has been developed in a strain of animals which had very little natural tendency to develop the disease. If there had been any congenital or hereditary characters in the development of these carcinomas, it did not appear in these experiments of Bagg's. He has watched this group of animals for thirteen years and has found a very low incidence of cancer, so I think that these experiments offer a somewhat difficult problem to those who believe in the congenital or hereditary incidence of cancer.

There was no question that Ewing's article was aimed at Maud Slye and her few supporters. As more researchers produced data that conflicted with Maud's findings, the controversy went on. Maud kept repeating that the type of product within a strain of mice depended on the matings within that strain. She compared this to a chemical result, which depended, of course, on what chemical combinations were made. If zinc and sulfuric acid were combined, there was one result; if zinc was combined with hydrochloric acid, there would be a different result. Thus, if she mated an albino mouse with a red mouse, she would get one type of offspring. If she mated the same albino mouse with a gray mouse, she would get a different type of offspring.

The percentage of any inheritable character, including cancer, could be changed in one mating in a strain of mice, according to the mating made. Maud warned that the greatest caution was necessary to obtain complete biologic control in any effort to discover the relation that experimental procedures of any kind bore to the causation of any type or location of cancer. The same caution was necessary in relating the basic facts of cancer heredity to experimental results. Any assumption that the fixed percentages of cancer could permanently define a heterozygous strain of mice—or any group or any individuals of such a strain—had to be discarded if the answer to whether cancer was a hereditary disease was to be obtained.

Maud believed that it would be impossible to get the right idea about heredity and cancer unless researchers regarded strains of mice as being plastic in every generation. Strains of mice were susceptible to change by one mating of the right kind, and the change could range from 100 percent of a character to 50 percent or zero percent. Strains of mice were also susceptible to being changed by a series of matings to any percentage desired by the researcher. If this were not true, and if strains were fixed in the percentage of inheritable characters they carried, then there would be no such thing as heredity, Maud asserted. And any new hybrid mating would bring nothing to the strain, since the new individual would have no new genes to offer.

That there were gaps in the existing knowledge of heredity and cancer Maud was the first to agree. However, she insisted, these gaps did not entitle researchers to deny a scientifically demonstrated fact, just because they could not make that fact agree with their own particular discovery or theory. Yet many researchers were doing just that when it came to Maud Slye's work and conclusions.

In cancer research, as in all other fields of scientific endeavor, all the facts had to be consistent with every other fact. "If it should eventually be possible to produce experimental cancer in every subject," Maud told a group of physicians, "this would not disprove the inheritability of cancer any more than the fact of inheritability of cancer proves that it must be impossible to produce cancer experimentally in every subject."

Actually, no biologist had ever made such an assertion. There had to be a third fact that harmonized with the other two. This third fact was already evident in the highly destructive nature of the experimental agents used; such as tar, which might well have destroyed the cancer-resistant mechanism or any other body mechanism in subjects on which the destructive agents were used. Spontaneous cancers did not arise in every individual, not in the human species nor in lower animals under identical conditions. This fact demonstrated that there was a cancer-resistant mechanism present in some members of every species. No amount of experimentally produced cancer could offset this fact, concluded Maud.

Maud again reminded scientists and physicians that if cancer should eventually be demonstrated to be a specific infection, this would not disprove its inheritability any more than the fact that the inheritability of cancer definitely proves that cancer is not a specific infection. Once again, there had to be a third factor, in addition to heredity and infection, and this third factor was readily seen in the organic response to various types of stimulation or irritation. This was true whether the irritant was a specific germ or anything else, although, Maud admitted, there were variations in the inheritance behavior. Apparently these variations had a bearing on the causes of various diseases.

Her reports in the medical journals and lectures to scientists and physicians won Maud a few converts, but the bulk of the scientific community remained unconvinced about the inheritability of cancer. These skeptics kept repeating that perhaps Maud's conclusions about the inheritability of cancer might apply to her mice, but they did not apply to human beings. Maud kept repeating that that argument had been settled by the fact of evolution. Similar tissues derived in the course of evolution from the same ancestry must respond in the same way as the ancestral tissues to the same types of stimulation. Only in such a way could an unbroken series of organisms evolve each from the other. As for those scientists who could not accept the evolutionary evidence, Maud suggested that their only recourse was to start research to produce data for the investigation of heredity in human beings.

The refusal or reluctance of scientists to accept Maud Slye's theories and conclusions on the inheritability of cancer was well within the long pattern established in the scientific world. For many centuries, science had been harsh on its dreamers, innovators, and revolutionists who came up with new theories, experiments, or treatments that contradicted what was accepted at the time or that threatened to shake the foundations of a branch of medicine or field of science. Great obstacles were often thrust into the paths of these scientific "deviates." Their work was attacked in the scientific journals and ridiculed in the public press. Only when the skeptics and opponents of a new theory or treatment were bombarded with irrefutable evidence was the new work accepted by the entire scientific community.

Most of the great scientists of the past and their work were subjected to attack and, in some cases, to censorship by their scientific peers: Lazzaro Spallanzani, the Italian naturalist, and his efforts to disprove the theory of spontaneous generation; Robert Koch, the German bacteriologist, who isolated the bacteria causing tuberculosis, anthrax, and Asian cholera; Louis Pasteur, the French chemist and bacteriologist, and his great work on immunization; Pierre Paul Emile Roux, the French physician and bacteriologist, who sought to develop an antitoxin against the child-killing disease, diptheria; Paul Ehrlich, the German bacteriologist and immunologist, who developed an antisyphilitic agent, the famous compound "606"; and even Maud Slye's contemporary, Marie Curie, discoverer of radium. All of these had at one time or another been ridiculed or vilified in the scientific journals and the public press. And Maud Slye was another scientific revolutionist who had to run the gauntlet that science ostensibly set up to protect humanity.

Although the critical attacks on Maud Slye's work and conclusions were sometimes tinged with personal invective, they were, on the whole, still within professional bounds. Whatever criticism had been aimed at Maud so far was well within the rights of scientists to question the validity of new theories, new experiments, and new conclusions. But the intent and tone of the attack on Maud Slye and her research were to change as the cancer-and-inheritance controversy went on and on. They were to become more vehement, more penetrating, and more personal.

SIX

The American Society for the Control of Cancer held a meeting to discuss cancer and cancer control at Lake Mohonk, near New Paltz, New York, in April of 1926. Eminent physicians and cancer researchers from all over the country had been invited to attend the meeting, and a number of important papers on cancer control were scheduled for delivery and discussion.

Maud Slye was invited to the meeting, but she had not been asked to deliver a report or read a paper about her research on cancer inheritability. Maud had been at odds with some members of the Society for some time, and her omission as a speaker was not unexpected.

Also among the physicians and researchers gathered at Lake Mohonk was Professor James Ewing, distinguished Professor of Pathology at Cornell Medical College, who had adopted a middle-of-the-road stand as far as Maud Slye's controversial research was concerned.

Paper after paper was read to the physicians and researchers, and lively discussions followed each one. Then, when a discussion centered on cancer control, Maud requested permission to speak. Some conferees thought Maud should not be allowed to speak to the group, since she was not an official delegate, but after a round of approvals and objections, she was finally granted permission to address the members of the Society. She gave a brief introduction of her mouse-breeding project, her experiments, and the conclusions drawn from the data. Then she told the conferees that since there was no known cure for cancer, she believed it was possible to control cancer on the basis of the knowledge she had amassed from her extensive study of the inheritability of cancer in mice.

At first there was complete silence. Then some conferees exchanged glances. Others shrugged as though to dismiss what she had told them. A few shook their heads in denial of Maud's conclusions. Finally, several physicians stood up and with loud objections told Maud that she was wrong; cancer was not hereditary and it could not be controlled by present means, no matter what her tests with mice demonstrated. These rebukes led to more heated discussion, until a physician from Toronto demanded that the Society take steps to assure the public that cancer was not hereditary. Others seconded his demand.

Maud was both startled and dismayed by the reaction of the Toronto physician and some of the other conferees. She felt the opposition was unwarranted, especially when the facts were examined. But she could easily see that many of the conferees, particularly the ones who were protesting the loudest to what she had said, would not examine the facts. She attempted to allay the fears of the Toronto physician, telling him that she had emphasized time and time again that the susceptibility to cancer was a recessive character, not a dominant one. "This is most encouraging," she declared, "for it means that large numbers of individuals are by inheritance exempt from the possibility of cancer."

But her opponents were not to be mollified by this so-called encouraging fact, and they demanded that the Society put out a "statement of facts and opinions on cancer" which would be agreed to by the participants in the conference. This demand was put to a vote and passed. First, the delegates worked on a preamble to a white paper on cancer and cancer control. The final version stated:

Although the present state of knowledge of cancer is not sufficient to permit of the formulation of such procedures for the suppression of this malady as have been successfully employed for the control of infectious diseases, there is enough well-established fact and sound working opinion concerning the prevention, diagnosis, and treatment of cancer to save many lives, if this information is carried properly into effect.

In discussing what was to go into the body of the Society's statement on cancer, the conferees agreed that the cause of cancer was not completely understood, Maud Slye's research notwithstanding. They also agreed that for all practical purposes cancer was not to be regarded as an infectious or contagious disease. After considerable and heated debate, a statement was included that said that cancer itself was not hereditary, although a certain predisposition or susceptibility to cancer was apparently transmitted through inheritance.

Nevertheless, whatever concession was made to Maud Slye's conclusions was considerably weakened by another and more cautious statement, which said that although a susceptibility to cancer might be transmitted through inheritance, this did not mean that because one's parent or a member of the family suffered from cancer, the disease would necessarily appear in other persons of the same or succeeding generation. With this statement, the Society neatly straddled the fence. It did not totally accept or deny Maud Slye's findings and conclusions. Maud was too astonished at the moment to raise an objection, and the statement became part of the Society's white paper on cancer.

The conferees spent a great deal of time discussing the diagnosis and treatment of cancer. Ultimately, two important concluding statements for the white paper were composed and agreed upon by the delegates. One statement called for more emphasis to be placed on distributing definite, useful, and practical knowledge about cancer. This knowledge should not be confused or hidden by mere theories or experimental work. Here was an obvious admonition for Maud Slye and other cancer researchers who were conducting cancer experiments and issuing conclusions that were not only questionable, according to the fundamentalists in the American Society for the Control of Cancer, but alarming to the general public. The other concluding statement of the paper pointed out two directions in which scientists should work for cancer control, namely, the promotion of research to increase existing knowledge of cancer and the practical use of cancer data already on hand.

At the close of the conference, Professor Ewing told the delegates that he believed Maud Slye had made a great contribution to the knowledge of cancer. There were nods of approval from the more moderate members of the Society, men who were at least willing to acknowledge the years of hard work and dedication that Maud had spent on cancer research. But the fundamentalists remained silent after Ewing's announcement. They were not about to endorse Ewing's accolade or officially honor Maud for her work.

The schism that existed in the field of cancer research did not escape the newspaper reporters who covered the conference at Lake Mohonk. The reporters were given copies of the Society's white paper on cancer and cancer control, but they sought out Maud Slye as the opponent of the fundamentalist group within the cancer-research field. When asked what she thought about the statement issued by the Society, Maud replied that she was unhappy with the decision not to inform the public that the tendency to cancer was inherited. She blamed the fundamentalists within the Society, particularly Francis Carter Wood, for the decision to withhold the information. She emphasized that more than eighteen years of research with her mice in the laboratory in the Sprague Memorial Institute in Chicago had definitely established that cancer was an inheritable disease. The public, she said, should so be informed, because such knowledge could be in itself a tool or measure in the control of cancer.

Maud described to the reporters the experiments in which she had introduced cancer heredity into a strain of mice, and explained how she had then been able to prevent cancer from appearing in the strain for twenty-five generations. She told them that cancer might remain hidden in human inheritance for just as many generations. When one of the parents had a pure cancer-resistant inheritance, the disease did not come to the surface in the children, but when both parents inherited a latent tendency to cancer, the offspring might develop the disease.

The reporters pressed her for more information, firing off question after question. As was to be expected, the tar-and-cancer question came up. Maud was used to the question, for it was dredged up at every medical or scientific meeting she attended. She explained to the reporters that the fact that cancer appeared in response to local irritation, such as the application of coal tar, indicated that it was an abnormal regenerative process. The lack of a definite mechanism in the tissue to regulate this regenerative process in repairing the wound was the hereditary predisposing quality.

Maud concluded the interview by stating that in the case of human beings it was impossible to analyze the tendency of anyone to acquire cancer because of the tradition of monogamy. However, it was important to remember that even freedom in the family from cancer for several generations was not a sure indication that a tendency to the disease was not latent.

Francis Carter Wood did not attend the conference, so the reporters interviewed some of the other fundamentalists in the American Society for the Control of Cancer. Their argument was similar to that always put forth by Wood. It was simply this: Maud Slye's mouse experiments might have demonstrated cancer inheritability in mice, but they did *not* demonstrate cancer inheritance in human beings. As far as the fundamentalists were concerned, Maud Slye's animal experiments proved nothing in regard to cancer and heredity in the human species.

After the Lake Mohonk conference, physicians and scientists in different parts of the country paid more attention to Maud Slye's research. Maud was invited to lecture to members of various medical and scientific groups on her research. These were not organized lecture tours like those made by Marie Curie when she came to America in 1921. Nor did Maud Slye have a public-relations agent to promote her and her work in the American press, as Marie Curie had on her trip to America. Maud simply accepted invitations to talk about her work when such appearances would not interfere with her all-important research.

Although the members of various western medical academies and societies did not all endorse or accept Maud's conclusions about the inheritability of cancer, they did make her an honorary member. They recognized her not so much for her controversial hypothesis and conclusions, but for the dedicated and determined effort she had put into years of research in one of the longest scientific projects known.

When the American College of Physicians held its annual meeting in New Orleans, Maud was invited to make a report on her work. She told the assembled physicians that her experiments with mice did have significance for the human race, despite what the physicians might have heard to the contrary. At the conclusion of her talk, she asked the American College of Physicians to establish a program for collecting and collating human cancer data that were based on case histories and autopsies. She declared that the medical world had moved blindly for too long in the field of cancer research and control. Now was the time to gather concrete statistical data on cancer incidence and to keep that data flowing into a cancer-research bureau.

Maud told the physicians that if they would set up a bureau

of human cancer statistics in Chicago, she would be glad to serve as the caretaker of the records and statistics gathered by physicians. Think of what such an organization would do to increase the knowledge about cancer, she exclaimed to the physicians. If such a bureau could maintain permanent recorded examination-findings on each living individual in the United States and the same kind of records for all the individuals who had died from cancer, there would be an invaluable bank of scientific data on cancer within three generations. The data amassed should include matings of double-cancerous parentage, matings of double-noncancerous parentage, matings of noncancerous individuals with hybrid carriers, matings of cancerous individuals with hybrid carriers, and double-hybrid matings. This was what she had done with her mice. If it was done for human beings, the accumulated data would provide an important tool for the control of cancer.

Several physicians pointed to the major barrier in setting up such a bureau: human autopsies for the purpose of obtaining data on cancer. They said that Maud and other researchers had no difficulty in conducting autopsies on mice dead from cancer or other disease, but it was a different story when it came to human beings. Autopsies were usually reserved for those individuals who had died as a result of violence or poisoning, or under suspicious circumstances. Furthermore, there were all kinds of objections to conducting autopsies, ranging from religious scruples to plain horror on the part of relatives.

Maud was well aware of the opposition to autopsies. She also knew that the subject was a touchy one among many members of the American College of Physicians. Still, she did not avoid the issue. She spoke to the point, reminding the physicians that though the dead were sacred, it was crucial for the living that autopsies be conducted on individuals who had died from cancer. If the public could be made to see the need for such autopsies and allow them to be done, it would be possible to gather information that would ultimately prove to be the most powerful tool ever wrought for the prevention of cancer. Furthermore, by using the correct selective methods, it might even be possible to eliminate cancer as a scourge of human beings, as she had done in the hundreds of mouse families in her laboratory.

When Maud had finished speaking, the physicians had many questions. She reponded to them all in her quiet manner, carefully explaining a technical point or clarifying an issue. Then a motion was made to appoint a committee to study Maud's plan for a bureau of human cancer statistics, as it was referred to by the physician making the motion. The motion was seconded, and the physicians unanimously voted to study Maud's plan. A committee was appointed to investigate the feasibility of setting up such a bureau and to report its findings to the American College of Physicians. Some of the members were so impressed by Maud Slye's tremendous research project and findings that they talked about recommending her for the Nobel Prize in Medicine.

But neither a bureau of human cancer statistics nor the recommendation for the Nobel Prize in Medicine ever materialized. Maud's opponents were instrumental in putting an end to these two dreams. For a variety of reasons, personal and professional, a number of physicians and researchers sought to discredit Maud and her work. Clarence Cook Little, who had become the president of the University of Michigan, severely criticized Maud's research and conclusions in an article published in the *Journal of Cancer Research*.

After Little had left Harvard University, he had served in the United States Army during World War I. Following his discharge from the army, he had spent four years at the Station for Experimental Evolution in the Carnegie Institution at Cold Spring Harbor, New York, and three years as president of the University of Maine. He had published a number of scientific papers in prestigious medical and scientific journals. However, at the time that Maud suggested the establishment of a bureau of cancer statistics, Little was not an active member of the American Society for Cancer Research, nor had he published anything on cancer for a number of years. Nevertheless, Little became one of the leaders of the opposition to Maud Slye's cancer research and her conclusions on cancer inheritability.

Little's criticism of Maud's work served to fan the fires of the cancer-and-heredity controversy into larger flames. More physicians and scientists joined in the attack on Maud. One scientist, who had originally accepted Maud's conclusion that cancer susceptibility was due to a recessive character, denounced it as erroneous and joined the fundamentalists. Not only had this scientist previously endorsed Maud's work, but he had constantly tried to identify himself with her research. He apparently did not want to be found on the other side of the fence, commented Maud. Later, the scientist denied ever saying that cancer susceptibility was due to a recessive character.

Maud remained in her mouse laboratory, trying to shut out the deluge of criticism, some of which was now amounting to attacks on her personality. She was bitterly disappointed over the failure of the American College of Physicians to set up a bureau for human cancer statistics, a measure that she felt could have been a major breakthrough in the fight against cancer. She hid her disappointment in not being nominated for the Nobel Prize in Medicine. What disappointment she experienced—the sting of the personal attacks on her, the mounting hostility to her work, the frustrations—these she set down in her poems.

Criticism of Maud and her work was not only published in medical and scientific journals by her detractors and opponents, but was also expressed in letters written to her as well as vocally whenever she appeared at a meeting. One Chicago physician wrote to her, setting down a number of questions regarding cancer and heredity, and providing some answers to his own questions. Of course, this reflected his obvious opposition to Maud's conclusions. Maud answered the letter, pointing out some of the flaws in his opinions about cancer and heredity.

The matter did not rest there, though. The physician sent another letter to Maud in which he denounced her and her conclusions on the inheritability of cancer. His opening paragraph set the tone for the letter:

Dear Miss Slye:
I wish to thank you for answering my inquiries concerning the heredity of cancer. It is very illuminating as to the quality of the scientific mind. If you can reach conclusions so quickly as to my beliefs, no doubt something of the same quality is included in your conclusions as to the heredity of cancer.
A conclusion that will not bear inquiry is not a very scientific conclusion.
I am not doubting your facts—but I do doubt your conclusions, and so do others. You did a cruel, dastardly and unscientific thing in broadcasting to the world that cancer is hereditary. In the present stage such things should be for the scientific man only. To destroy all hope in patients with cancer or supposed cancer, as well as to get their children morbid on the subject as to the likelihood of their children having cancer, is to engender an untold amount of mental torture in the supposed victims and you cannot be too roundly condemned for such doings. Should you wish to discuss the cancer question in a scientific spirit instead of an egotistical one, I shall be pleased to hear from you, otherwise please consider this correspondence closed.

Maud was stung by this letter. Though she could understand a difference of opinion as to her conclusions on cancer heredity, she could not understand the reason for the physician's scathing personal attack and his condemnation of her making known to the public the fact that cancer was an inheritable disease. The physician's accusations were not justified; moreover, he had been just as unscientific in his conclusions about cancer and heredity as he claimed she had been.

Maud did not continue the correspondence. The physician was entitled to his opinion, of course, and she to hers. And if any "egotistical spirit" was involved in the exchange of letters, Maud believed it was the male ego. Just the same, the attack on her motive for informing the public about the inheritability of cancer bothered her for a long time.

But Maud received other letters—letters from physicians and scientists who approved her stand on the inheritability of cancer or congratulated her on the immense and important research project that she had been conducting for nearly twenty years. "Will you permit me to express my admiration of the paper you published in the *Journal of the American Medical Association*," wrote the editor of *The Journal of Heredity*, published by the American Genetic Association in Washington, D.C. "It is one of the clearest and most cogent statements of the sort that I have read in a long time, and precisely what the medical profession needs to hear," continued the editor. "Both genetics and eugenics are suffering because most physicians never grasp the fundamental principles of the study of heredity as it applies to disease." The paper by Maud Slye that the editor referred to in his letter was "Some Misconceptions Regarding the Relation of Heredity to Cancer and Other Diseases."

A prominent New York City physician wrote to Maud, expressing his admiration for the same paper, which she had read before its publication to members of the American Society for Cancer Research. "I have long been convinced," wrote the physician, "of the truth of your conclusions, and am glad that you came out so openly and so thoroughly in showing that the opposition has all clearly been based upon 'prejudice and preconceived opinion' instead of upon the facts.''

The mixed reception given to her research findings and conclusions by the scientific community continued to perplex Maud. She knew that every scientist must be prepared to back up his conclusions with hard facts. She had the facts in the voluminous records kept on each mouse and each strain of mice for many generations, and she was particularly disturbed by the white paper that had evolved from the conference on cancer and cancer control held by the American Society for the Control of Cancer.

In a letter to Dr. George Soper, managing director of the American Society for the Control of Cancer, Maud stated her objections to some of the statements in the white paper on cancer and cancer control.

The first statement of the pronouncement [wrote Maud] is misleading and in spirit entirely contradicts the second statement, and nullifies it; while the final statement that "this does not mean that if the parents and grandparents are both cancerous the children will be susceptible." [Maud did not complete this sentence, but the next sentence relates to it.] This, my dear Dr. Soper, is entirely untrue, and I shall not be able to allow it to stand without criticism, however much I might wish to do so for the sake of harmony and agreement.

It is a very great pity, as I see it, that a piece of scientific knowledge of such momentous value to humanity cannot get itself heard. Not only that, but that it must be categorically denied. This denial does not protect humanity, since humanity cannot be protected by contradicting natural law. As I see it, humanity would be incalculably benefitted by knowing and observing this profound natural law.

She lamented the attitude of the American Society for the Control of Cancer regarding her conclusions on cancer and heredity.

> I am distressed [she wrote] that with my best efforts, I cannot impress the Society for the Control of Cancer, and I suppose that I must therefore continue to stand outside the pale of that Society; but I cannot accept its pronouncement in its present shape. I am writing this to you at length, in order not to take you by surprise in my next publication, and because I would so much appreciate a harmony with that Society.

But Maud's proffering of an olive branch was spurned by Dr. Soper. Instead, he took her to task for some of the statements in her letter. He reminded her that she had been present at the conference at Lake Mohonk when the pronouncement or resolution on cancer and cancer control was prepared and approved. Why didn't she object to it then? She could have registered any protest or voiced any criticism or offered any amendment, added the doctor. Since she had not made any protest or offered any amendment to the resolution, he and others assumed that Maud had no objections to the resolution as approved by the delegates.

Soper thought Maud's letter was "the more unreasonable and unfair because of the conversation which you and I had when we first met at Mohonk." He was referring to an encounter with Maud in which he had told her he was making a careful study of her work and reports, as well as those of other cancer investigators. He wanted to form a fair and independent judgment on the subject of cancer and heredity. Therefore, he had asked Maud to suspend her "hostilities toward our Society" until he had an opportunity to complete his study. Soper thought Maud had agreed to this, and had counted on her cooperation. When Maud raised no objection

to the resolution drawn up at Lake Mohonk, he had thought
she was cooperating in response to his request.

> Now, several weeks later, [wrote Soper] you send me a
> letter to say that you disagree with the resolution and that
> if it is used as intended, you will attack it in your very
> next publication. This is incomprehensible, except on the
> ground that you do not clearly recall the facts. My belief
> that your memory is at fault is supported by the fact that
> you seriously misquote the resolution and misstate the
> circumstances under which it was passed. . . .
> Permit me to express the hope, that upon careful read-
> ing of the paragraph on heredity, and further reflections
> on the whole matter, you will decide to follow the course
> which I proposed to you at Mohonk—and which, I am
> sure—will produce a better understanding of your work
> than could be produced by the criticisms which you now
> propose to make.

And to refresh Maud's memory, Dr. Soper included with
his letter a copy of the resolution made at Lake Mohonk.

Unfortunately, Maud did misquote the statements in the
resolution; that is, she did not quote them verbatim. However, she did have the gist of the paragraph on cancer and
heredity, particularly the statements that greatly and cau-
tiously qualified her conclusions about the inheritability of
cancer. Actually, what Soper had hoped to avoid at the
Mohonk conference was a confrontation between Maud Slye
and those physicians and scientists who opposed her conclusions about cancer inheritability. In short, he did not want
Maud to rock the boat. Therefore, he had come up with the
compromise of having Maud hold off with her objections until
he had made a thorough study of her work.

Unquestionably, Maud had not been welcome at the
Mohonk conference, as far as a large number of the members
of the American Society for the Control of Cancer were con-

cerned. Similarly, Maud had not been overjoyed at having to contend with them. But she had been willing to avoid an open battle at the conference, as requested by Dr. Soper, and she had kept at least part of the bargain made with him. Except when she discussed her work with mice, she had remained quiet at the meetings. She had also refrained from objecting to the controversial paragraph in the resolution.

Later, after she had returned to Chicago and thought about it, Maud realized what had taken place at Lake Mohonk. A statement about cancer and heredity—one that said considerably less than what Maud Slye had been reporting—had been proposed and approved, with no objection from Maud Slye, who was present when the resolution was unanimously passed by the delegates!

Back in her mouse laboratory, Maud was not only dismayed but angered at what had happened to her at Lake Mohonk. She had been maneuvered by Dr. Soper. By not seeking a confrontation with the fundamentalists she had assumed a position of nonprotest, and by remaining silent when the resolution was passed, she had given tacit approval to the entire pronouncement on cancer. In brief, she had been neutralized.

The professional sniping at Maud continued, even though the great value of her work was becoming more apparent to moderate physicians, geneticists, and other scientists. Some of the criticisms and skepticism aimed at Maud and her conclusions about cancer inheritability were based on scientific principles or arguments. They were leveled by scientists who believed that they had a right to question her research methods and conclusions.

Maud did not object to professional criticism, especially when it was presented in a scientific and objective manner. She had enough confidence in her ability as a researcher and in the vast collection of facts derived from her extended mouse-breeding program to answer any valid criticisms. It was the scientists who abandoned professionalism, who ignored objectivity and resorted to prejudice and personal vilification, arguing incessantly, in their attacks on her and her work—they were the ones she feared.

Whatever the motive behind the criticism of her work, Maud's innate sensitivity did not let her forget them. However, she did not let them interfere with her experiments; she kept on with her mouse research, determined to produce more proof, proof that even the most dedicated skeptic would have to accept.

Only in the quiet of her house across the street from the mouse laboratory did she feel the stings of the attacks on her personality usually made by scientists who resented that she was gaining recognition while they remained obscure, or by those who were annoyed that the leading researcher on cancer and heredity was a woman. What and how she felt about all these things—the lack of understanding of what she was trying to do, the attacks on her and her work—she set down in a poem that would some day form part of a book:

For you may ask a scientist
Just what he meant—he has no privacy
Of owned intent or any outcome,
And may be bombed with prejudice,
With inquisitions and with weapons fixed
For his full overthrow. But not an artist,
You may not ask questions of his way nor any purposes,
And if you cannot see the colors
That glint upon his path or the white light
That burns from far—so much the worse for you!
He is no target for your onslaught
And his way is all his own.

SEVEN

The Columbus Academy of Medicine invited Maud Slye to Ohio to speak to the members about her work. Maud accepted and delivered a lecture on the inheritability of cancer, as demonstrated by the results obtained in her mouse laboratory. She also talked about the great need for more statistics on human cancer. She told the Columbus physicians that all physicians and scientists were welcome to visit her laboratory in Chicago and to see her many generations of cancerous and noncancerous mice. She mentioned that a number of researchers had already visited the laboratory. At first these scientists had been highly critical and very skeptical about her work and conclusions, but most of them, Maud added, had left her laboratory as believers.

In general, Maud's lecture was well received by the Columbus physicians, although not all of them were convinced that her conclusions were correct.

At a later meeting of the Columbus Academy of Medicine, a physician told the group that there was some reason to doubt the sincerity of Maud's invitation to visit her laboratory. When pressed for the reason, the physician said that he had been informed that some researchers had gone to Maud's laboratory, but when they asked to see her statistical records on the cancer-inheritability experiments, she had refused them access to the records. Not only did she refuse to let the scientists see the data, but when they insisted that she give them free access to the records, she broke down and cried, saying that they were trying to prove she was lying about her research results.

This astonishing accusation was passed on to Maud Slye by a friendly physician in the Columbus Academy of Medicine. He wrote to Maud, telling her that he was informing her about the allegation because he felt that she should have the opportunity to defend herself against the charge. If Maud would send him a letter, confirming or denying the allegation, he would read the letter to the members of the Columbus Academy of Medicine at their next meeting. The physician added a statement to the effect that he was risking the wrath of a very influential member of the Columbus medical group by writing to Maud and telling her about the charge, and in asking for her side of the story. "But," he wrote in conclusion, "I am always on the side of right and willing to champion the cause of one who is not present to answer for himself."

Now the charge made against Maud was two-pronged: (1) that she had refused certain researchers access to her records and statistical data on her cancer-and-inheritance experiments, and, (2) that she had "broken down and cried" when the researchers insisted that she allow them to see the experimental data.

The first part of the charge, if true, was a grave one, for it meant that Maud had acted against all professional standards in refusing the researchers access to her data. In the scientific world, it was the standard practice for researchers to make their procedures, methods, and findings available to investigators. Only when another researcher had conducted a similar experiment—that is, duplicated the original experiment, using the initial investigator's methods and techniques—was it possible to test the validity of an experiment and the conclusions made from it. Maud was charged with violating this time-honored scientific practice.

The second part of the allegation, that Maud had broken down and cried when the visiting researchers asked to see her records, was equally serious, because it cast doubt on her scientific conduct and, more insidiously, on her emotional stability. A scientist was not supposed to break down and cry when asked for his or her experimental data. A scientist was not supposed to claim that he or she was being persecuted or accused of lying about research results just because another investigator asked to see the statistics and data. Worst of all, a scientist was not supposed to act in a womanish manner.

Maud was indignant when she read the letter from the Columbus physician. She was accustomed by this time to challenges and attacks from scientists and had answered them one by one, either in a letter or in an article in the medical and scientific journals. Usually the criticisms that required an answer from her dealt with the procedures, methods, and findings of her mouse experiments. But these new charges struck deeper. They took on a personal tone that by far exceeded any that she had received before. What bothered her most of all was the charge that she had broken down and cried, for she had never forgotten the nervous breakdown she had suffered during her undergraduate days at the University of Chicago. So far, it had never been used against her.

In all her years as a researcher, Maud had always maintained a calm, reserved approach to her work. The people who worked with her or listened to her lectures were usually impressed with her great patience and self-control. Yet behind this cool exterior, this calm façade, was an extremely sensitive nature. Yes, Maud could weep. She could weep for the loss of one of her mice, and at the fall of a sparrow, and at the passing of a friend. But these were private tears. They were not to be seen by colleagues or enemies who might not understand them or distort their meaning. As for Maud's weeping for herself or for some real or fancied wrong, she had too much control to weep before anyone. That kind of weeping she reserved for the darkness of her bedroom or the verses of her poetry.

Maud waited until her anger over the letter had subsided

before she answered the Columbus physician. When she was able to view the charge in its proper perspective, she wrote to him and expressed her amazement at the charges made before the Columbus Academy of Medicine. "So far as I know," she wrote, "no reputable physician or scientist that has ever wished to visit my laboratory has been refused." Nor had she ever refused anyone access to her research data.

She asked the physician to give her the name of the "influential member" of the Columbus Academy of Medicine who apparently was spreading malicious gossip about her, or "retailing this figment of the imagination." She wanted to know who the physicians or scientists were who allegedly had been denied admission to her laboratory and records. Also, when did this incident take place?

She followed this up with a series of penetrating questions: Who were the investigators? What were they investigating? By whom were they sent or what organization did they represent? And what was the purpose of their supposed visit? In view of the charges against her, Maud said, these were pertinent questions to which she was entitled answers. As for the charge that she broke out in tears, Maud told the physician that anyone acquainted with her would realize such a statement was a lie. Whatever her reception of an investigator might be, she declared, it would not be tears!

Thorough investigator that she was, Maud checked the Columbus physician's information with another Columbus physician, asking him to clarify the matter. She queried him on the credentials of the first physician, asking if he was a member in good standing of the Columbus Academy of Medicine. She mentioned that she did not remember meeting this particular physician when she lectured before the Academy. She also wanted to know the identity of the "influential member" of the Academy who was spreading lies about her. She wanted this information so that she could write directly to the man. "I have never heard a more ridiculously unfounded or a more malignant insinuation," she exclaimed in her letter to the second Columbus physician. "And I hope that the originator will not remain in obscurity." She ended the letter by saying that she was sorry to have had her most pleasant memory of her visit to the Columbus Academy of Medicine marred by such an unpleasantry.

Maud had no option but to track down the source of the charges made against her. Not only were the charges serious because of Maud's standing as a scientist, but also because of the nature of her research. If the charges were true and Maud had refused to admit researchers into her laboratory or denied them access to her experimental data, other scientists would infer that she had something to hide or that her experiments could not be duplicated, a charge that had already been made. As for the allegation that she had wept when confronted by the supposed visitors, this charge also had to be put down quickly. It was an obvious attempt to show Maud Slye as an overly emotional person and implied that all women scientists were prone to emotionalism.

In investigating the source of the charges, Maud turned up some interesting facts. First of all, the trail to the originator of the charge was a circuitous one. It did not end in Columbus, Ohio, but continued on to the Institute for Cancer Research in New York City. Dr. Carl Hyer, the second Columbus physician to whom Maud wrote after receiving the original letter setting down the charge, explained to her how the charge had started.

It began shortly after Maud had lectured before the Columbus Academy of Medicine. At the next meeting of the Academy, the physicians listened to the reading of a paper on cancer of the stomach. During the general discussion that followed, someone mentioned Maud Slye's work with cancer in mice. Then another physician, a surgeon, mentioned that he had been in New York City and had talked with Francis Carter Wood of the Institute for Cancer Research. Wood, according to the surgeon, said that he had not been able to reproduce Maud's results in his white rats, thus implying that what Maud had demonstrated in mice was not true for rats. The surgeon also told members of the Columbus Academy that some investigators encountered difficulty when they tried to check on Maud's research data. He further stated that when Maud was approached for her records and statistics and rigorously questioned about her research and findings, she broke down in tears.

Dr. Hyer tried to cool the situation by saying that members of the Columbus Academy of Medicine had a good impression of Maud and that there had been many favorable comments about the paper she had read before the group. He added that he would like Maud to send him an explanation of the situation and charges. If she did, he would read it in her behalf at the next meeting of the Academy. He would also look into the charges himself and write to Francis Carter Wood regarding his work with rats. Dr. Hyer emphasized that the situation was not "as bad as your apparent version of the incident" and that a statement from Maud regarding it would be satisfactory to all concerned.

Francis Carter Wood was the fundamentalist who had challenged Maud's findings and conclusions in the past. When Maud learned that the charges had more or less originated with him, she wrote to him and repeated what the two Columbus physicians had told her. Wood answered with the suggestion that she come to the Institute for Cancer Research and see the work being done there, instead of listening to "assorted gossip as to what I have said or have not said." He said that he would be very glad to show her the results of the Institute's cancer experiments and that she could draw her own conclusions.

When the charges made against Maud made the rounds of the scientific community, some physicians and scientists thought the whole matter was a "tempest in a teapot." But it was more than that, at least for Maud Slye. Her reputation as a research scientist was in jeopardy. Her professional integrity and her ability to be objective and emotionally stable during inquiries into her work had been questioned. Maud had no alternative but to prove the charges as false and to smoke out the person or persons who had instigated them. She also had the right to do so.

It was obvious to Maud and to those who admired her and respected her work that these charges were another attempt, albeit a more insidious one, to discredit her work and her standing as a competent scientist. Jealousy, spite, hatred, and deviousness were not limited to the artistic or commercial worlds or even the political world; they also existed in the scientific world which, like the other worlds, was composed of human beings. Scientists could be just as petty, spiteful, and vengeful as anyone else, particularly when fame or recognition was at stake.

The Columbus physician who first informed Maud of the charges wrote to her again, this time saying that he thought a public apology was due her. He mentioned that he would bring the matter up at a future meeting of the Columbus Academy of Medicine, but before he did, he wanted to be certain that an influential member of the group would be present at the meeting. He did not mention the name of this person, thus compounding the issue with secrecy.

Meanwhile, Maud wrote another letter to Francis Carter Wood, this time taking a more conciliatory attitude. She pointed out to Wood that the charges against her were made at a professional medical meeting. While the charges may or may not have been "assorted gossip," as Wood described them in his note to her, she never expected to hear that such statements had been made at a meeting of physicians. She told Wood that she regretted not having been able to visit his laboratory in the Institute of Cancer Research. As for his suggestion that she come to see the work being done at the

Institute, she replied that, unfortunately, it was not possible. "You know," she wrote, "we mere researchers are pretty poor and cannot take all of the trips we would like to take. Therefore, I fear I shall not be in New York again in the very near future. I would be very glad if you would tell me something briefly of the results referred to." Wood never answered her letter.

But the matter did not end there. The surgeon who had brought the subject up at the meeting of the Columbus Academy of Medicine now entered the arena. He informed the members of the Academy, a number of whom regarded Maud Slye's findings as being applicable to human beings, that there were many scientists who had attended the cancer conference at Lake Mohonk who did not agree with Maud's findings and conclusions. "Dr. Slye's opinion on heredity was not accepted by everybody," the surgeon told the members of the Academy. Furthermore, it was his understanding that her findings could not be applied to human beings. He again repeated the scene that was supposed to have taken place in Maud's laboratory, in which she had burst into tears when questioned by the visiting researchers, who were from the Institute for Cancer Research.

Maud learned about this latest development in a letter from the Columbus surgeon. He wrote that he had accepted Dr. Wood's statements at face value. He claimed that his only purpose in repeating them to the members of the Columbus Academy of Medicine was that he wanted them to take "a more sober view of the subject of heredity in human beings." He had not meant it to be a disparaging criticism of Maud's work. In the first place, he added, he was not qualified to criticize her research. Secondly, he never had such an intention because he held Maud and her work in the very highest regard.

If the Columbus surgeon thought highly of her work, Maud thought he had chosen a poor way to praise it. Although his efforts to explain his actions missed fire, he had at least indicated who had instigated the charges against her. Francis Carter Wood had not bothered to enlighten her.

However, Maud wanted more than just an oblique apology from the Columbus surgeon who, after all, had brought the subject up before the Columbus Academy of Medicine. She wrote him a letter, saying that she thought it strange that, while he had not been the originator of the gossip, he would use such an unprofessional method to criticize someone's work. "Consider for a moment," she wrote, "what you would think of it if I should announce at some scientific meeting—in commenting on your work on goiter" (the Columbus surgeon was a specialist in the field of goiter surgery)—"that when you were asked for your records, you burst into tears because of the implication against your veracity." Undoubtedly, Maud said, he would react the same way she did. "I am no more likely to take part in such an episode than you would be," she added. Then she asked him to withdraw his remarks before the Columbus Academy of Medicine.

As for her work being accepted by everybody in its application to human beings, Maud reminded the surgeon that no scientist could expect his work to be accepted by everybody. There were too many uninformed individuals for even the greatest truths to be universally accepted. Even the work of Charles Darwin, and the great scientists who preceded him, had not been accepted by everybody, nor were the works totally accepted at the time. Maud was alluding to the furor over evolution in some of the Southern states and the bitter controversy stirred up at the Monkey Trial in Tennessee.

Maud could not resist the temptation to send a copy of the Columbus surgeon's letter to Francis Carter Wood in New York. She included a note:

The enclosed copy of a letter from Dr. C. of Columbus, Ohio, explains itself. Rather small potatoes for a man of your professional standing, is it not? Reminds me of the old-fashioned old ladies' sewing circles, where they made clothes and tried to unmake reputations, doesn't it? I hope the scientific world is not going to adopt "tear gas" in its attacks.

Wood's response to Maud's note and the copy of the Columbus surgeon's letter to Maud was a terse message:

I am sorry I haven't had a chance to answer your letter of November 15th, which indeed proves that you have been listening to assorted gossip. I have no "representatives" and never sent one to your laboratory, and have not been in it myself except some time in 1911 or 1912, when we had a most amiable interview. So the accuracy of Dr. C.'s statement can be left to your judgment.

With this note, Wood neatly tossed the matter back into Maud's lap. She could either consider Dr. C.'s statement to be accurate or inaccurate. Wood had wriggled off the hook, if indeed he had been caught on it. Dr. C. in Columbus was the one who had aired the subject before the Columbus Academy of Medicine, not Dr. Wood.

Although Dr. Wood seemed to dismiss the matter with his note to Maud, Dr. C. had not. In another letter to Maud, he stated that he could not withdraw his remarks before the Academy. "I am very sorry to have to say to you that there is not a single word I can withdraw," he told Maud in a sharply written letter. "The remarks I made were those I wrote to you in my last letter and it would cast upon the honesty of my intentions a very grave doubt if I should withdraw them."

However, Dr. C. offered to read Maud's letter to him before the Academy. Her letter could stand as a denial of the charges. After all, that was what Maud wanted most: a more or less public denial. The surgeon objected to Maud's statement that his remarks to the members of the Academy about her and her work had been unprofessional, but he did agree that he had been thoughtless in presenting the charges to the Academy. He again asked Maud to try to understand his motives. After her lecture to the Academy, many members had been under the impression that cancer was hereditary in the human species, since Maud had so concluded from her experiments with mice. But Dr. C. did not consider her conclusions as being applicable to human beings.

Even though Dr. C. had stated in his previous letter that he was not qualified to criticize Maud's work, he proceeded to do so in his second letter. First, he said that inherited cancer in mice, to the extent Maud claimed her experiments to show, could not be demonstrated in rats, according to the experiments of Francis Carter Wood. Dr. C. regarded Wood as one of the most outstanding authorities on cancer research, not only in America but throughout the world. Therefore, stated Dr. C., the findings of Maud Slye with reference to her mice were not applicable to human beings, since they were not true for rats. In addition, nothing in Maud's work authorized her to generalize from mice to men.

Dr. C. reminded Maud that cancer heredity had not been clinically demonstrated in the human race. He and other physicians who saw a great deal of human cancer did not see any relationship between cancer in an individual's parentage and the cancer patient. Maud was using the word "heredity" rather promiscuously, said Dr. C. He understood the word, as applied to the line of research in which Maud was engaged, to mean the direct transmission of a pathological agent from parents to offspring. And he mentioned syphilis as an example of this kind of transmission.

It was true, he continued, that Maud had succeeded in rendering her mice susceptible to cancer grafts. (Dr. C. was in error. Maud had never worked with cancer grafts; all of the cancer produced in her mice resulted from spontaneous tumors.) Therefore, added Dr. C., all that Maud did in her experiments was to render her mice susceptible to cancer. That was all she was entitled to claim from her experiments. She did not, for example, explain how the susceptibility to cancer came about and, most important of all, she could not say what caused cancer.

Dr. C. went on taking Maud's work apart. Assuming that the same hereditary disposition to cancer could be demonstrated in human beings—and such a susceptibility had not as yet been shown—a predisposed human being *would have to come into contact with the causative agent of cancer before developing the disease.* Of course Maud had been able to control this factor by grafting cancers in her mice (again, Dr. C. was in error). But in the case of human beings, who could tell which individual would come into contact with the causative agent of cancer, even if heredity was a factor? Some individuals would, some would not. Thus, reasoned Dr. C., Maud's law of heredity and cancer in mice would fail when applied to human beings.

He suggested that Maud consider the research being conducted under the sponsorship of the Metropolitan Life Insurance Company. Researchers had investigated hundreds of thousands of cases of human cancer, trying to establish a relationship between cancer in ancestors and the patient with cancer. The finds were almost all negative. For all these reasons, therefore, Dr. C. felt that the members of the Columbus Academy of Medicine should not be left with the impression, created by Maud's claims, that cancer was hereditary in human beings. Once more, though Dr. C. was not qualified to judge Maud's experimental work, he did differ with her conclusions as applied to human beings.

Again, an accusing finger was pointed at Maud. Dr. C. told her that before she thrust such conclusions upon the public, she should make certain that she was not making a tragic mistake. She ought to realize that the life of people whose parents had died from cancer would be a real "hell on earth," if her conclusions should turn out to be true.

When Maud read Dr. C.'s letter, she was distressed and angry. She was distressed because the surgeon either did not understand her work or simply was too rigid in his thinking. She was angered by his closing remarks about her informing the public that cancer was hereditary because what he had written implied that she had no feelings, that she was insensitive, a coldhearted person who did not care what fear or panic she would cause with her cancer-and-heredity statements. That was the greatest sting of all the criticism leveled at her. And it was not justified. Whatever Maud Slye was, she was not an insensitive person. She knew the horrors of cancer, for she had seen massive tumors snuff the life out of hundreds of her mice. And she had wept silent tears at the death of each mouse.

EIGHT

Maud persisted in her efforts to have Dr. C. or another member of the Columbus Academy of Medicine set the record straight and clear her name of the charges. She had to have some kind of public vindication, since the charges had been made in public. Her integrity and veracity as a research scientist, not to mention her personal character, had been questioned. Some of her friends and associates thought she was making too much of the affair; they told her that she was paying too much attention to gossip. Everyone gossiped at one time or other, said her associates, and physicians and scientists were no exception. Maud was taking it all too seriously.

Perhaps what Dr. C. had repeated to the members of the Columbus Academy of Medicine might be construed as gossip, since he was repeating something told to him by Francis Carter Wood, who in turn was supposed to have repeated something told to him by visitors to Maud Slye's mouse laboratory. That much was evident from Dr. C.'s letters to Maud. But it was *how* Dr. C. had repeated the gossip that disturbed Maud. Had he merely mentioned the supposed laboratory scene to one or two of his associates and said that he had heard that her conclusions about cancer and heredity could not be applied to human beings, that action, although questionable in itself, might have been overlooked by Maud. But the alleged statements by Dr. Wood about the mysterious visitors to Maud's laboratory (whom Wood denied ever having sent to Maud's laboratory) had been presented before the assembled physicians of the Columbus Academy of Medicine. This was quite a different situation; it amounted to a public criticism of Maud Slye and her work. More than that, it constituted a public shaming of Maud Slye, the scientist and the woman.

Then there was the matter of those physicians and scientists who berated Maud for making public statements about the inheritability of cancer. They had accused her of being callous, egotistical, and insensitive to the feelings of people whose parents had died from cancer. They thought that even if she should be proved correct in her conclusions, she should keep that information within the boundaries of the scientific community. She had no right to make it public.

The charge that she was a callous and insensitive person continued to bother Maud, for it kept appearing, sometimes in the press, more often in letters from physicians who thought of her as a spinsterish woman scientist who cared more for theories and conclusions than she cared about human beings. They were wrong, of course. True, Maud had never married. She had had a love affair with an artist in her early years, but the artist had died, and Maud had dedicated her life to science. Nevertheless, beyond the wall of the scientific enclave, away from the unrelenting routine of research, she felt and reacted to life: to people, animals, sounds, smells, noises; to the joy of listening to great music; the satisfaction of painting a landscape; the peace that came in her garden.

She did not mix her two worlds, the narrow, confining world of science and the soul-searching world of the artist. She kept them separate. In the scientific world, despite what the mythical visitors to her laboratory said, Maud was the calm, competent, dedicated researcher. In the other world, the world of the artist, she released her feelings, frustrations, and anger in poetry, painting, and music. And always in the world away from the laboratory, she kept seeking for some answer to the riddle of life.

Maud's constant quest for the meaning of life fairly jumped out of the lines of her poetry. In her verses, she sang of love, nature, science, work, the turmoil of the city, and she wrote of dreams and yearnings:

Out of my youth I make my song
Singing, winging its flight through the sky
Out of my youth I cry
Making my song.
Out of my heart I make my song
Throbbing, sobbing itself to sleep and to dreams seek,
Out of my heart I speak
Making my song. . . .

She wrote about her disappointment in men, incorporating the frustrations and rejections of herself and her work:

I thought my treasure lay in the gift of men,
Valueing their verdict as of worth
To pick the riches of a life
And make appraisal of its deeds.
'Tis many years since then,
I walk alone now, and my treasure
Is only in my work,
For whose evalueing I search my soul,
Nor bring it ever to the marts of men.

Out of her deep compassion for living creatures, she wrote about a dead sparrow:

A dead little English sparrow
Grey as the winter ground
Its feathers were folded narrow
And smooth, and the wind around
Was futilely trying to start its gay flight;
It must have sunk in the cold last night.

I do not know where it slept last night,
Perhaps in some windswept tree,
And its little life dropped out of sight
Silently, painlessly.
A gay little cheerful bit of life
Has just closed down without struggle or strife.

Whatever the flaws of Maud's poetry, they revealed the inner soul of this sensitive woman.

I cannot sleep because the ice is on the trees,
And all the street lamps strike upon the white
And turn it into faery. I cannot sleep
Because each bush is heavy with its crystal load,
And every slightest twig and blade of grass
Reflects the lights of worlds. How shall I sleep?
Whose soul must travel to the outer space,
In worship of this origin of beauty.
O beauty that can rock the world,
Or dressed in crystal or enrobed in green,
How shall I sleep who hear the lucent sound
Of moving twigs and waving beauty boughs?

Maud's work was more than just an occupation; it was her life. Long ago, she had given herself up to the world of science. . . .

So many paths that lead!
'Twas not for me to go that happy road
Of flower-decked bride and mother
Whose rich arms clasped all her babies; and of Grandam
Beside her late life's fire, who sees her brood
Of second generation gather round her knee.
To be beguiled with tales,
A rosy firelight glow across her aged heart!

'Twas not for me to go that road of peace
My head against your breast when evening came. . . .

Her work flowed over into her other world at times:

A fertilized egg—a single cell
Homogeneous to any test we know to make,
Yet holding wrapped within its tiny sphere
All that can make a man.

Uniform everywhere—
By any trial uniform—and yet
From this one point will come one member of a body,
From this and this, another and another.

From this point the feet will come
To carry him through all the traveling,
Through all the wandering,
That makes a life.

From this point will come a heart
That beats with all the joy and all the pain,
With all the hope and all the hurt
That makes a life.

And here will come the brain,
Complex past our analysis,
A brain that builds the thoughts
That built a world.

A simple cell—small past unaided sight
So organized that every point within its tiny sphere
Has each its function perfected in time,
Or changed by interference!

These were some of the poems that Maud wrote in the stillness of her house across the street from her beloved laboratory and its city of mice. The poems were her solace, her balance wheel, and they enabled her to survive the attacks on her character and work. For an hour, for an evening, she could forget the name-calling, the skepticism, the harsh criticism of her work, and the distortion of truth that came out of some quarters of the scientific world. But in the morning, when she crossed the street to her laboratory and picked up the mail, it all came back again in a letter or a scientific journal.

Maud answered all the letters, just as she answered the last letter from Dr. C., the one in which he had set down his objections to her conclusions and censored her for making her conclusions known to the public. She opened her letter to Dr. C. by saying once more that he had acted in an unprofessional manner by repeating lies—or, more charitably, gossip—to the Columbus Academy of Medicine. "Your remarks were, in my opinion," she wrote, "unprofessional in that in order to strengthen your disagreement with my work, you used personal gossip which was an unqualified lie. Your disagreement with my work is perfectly permissible and troubles me not at all."

She stressed the fact that no work done at the Institute for Cancer Research, Columbia University, or at any other institution, had as yet been published which in any way refuted the findings and conclusions of her work. When such work was published, then it would be considered. Also, any work that did refute her conclusions would itself be open to criticism. Furthermore, she went on, Dr. C. apparently had not read her papers, especially those that showed the reasons for the biologic application of her conclusions on cancer and heredity to human beings.

She chided Dr. C. for his misuse of the term "heredity," saying that it was he who used the term promiscuously, not she. First of all, heredity in the human species could not be clinically demonstrated with the present means, just as insulin could not be clinically extracted from the human pancreas. She reminded him that syphilis, which he had used as an example of a hereditary disease, was not hereditary, but congenital. She suggested that he read her article, *Some Misconceptions Regarding the Relation of Heredity to Cancer and Other Diseases*, which discussed the misunderstanding and misuse of scientific terms.

A major error in Dr. C.'s criticism of Maud's conclusions was in saying that all she had succeeded in doing was to cause susceptibility to cancer grafts in her mice. Maud told him that none of the tumors that developed in hundreds of her mice had come as a result of cancer grafts. All of the tumors reported by her were spontaneous tumors that appeared during the natural life of the mice. There had been no artificial inducement of tumors in any of her mice, and there had been no other kind of interference with them except that of selective breeding. Thus, the tumors that arose in her mice did so spontaneously, just as they did in human beings. This fact had been stated in every paper Maud had published during the past sixteen years. Obviously, Dr. C. had not read them. Maud underscored one other point: she did not render the mice susceptible to cancer; *They were susceptible by nature.*

Maud admitted that Dr. C. was correct in stating that both mice and men predisposed to cancer probably had to come into contact with an irritating agent to provoke a neoplastic reaction. By the same reasoning, she argued, both cancer-susceptible mice and human beings could escape cancer by avoiding the type of irritation that could cause cancer. This fact was a most encouraging thing. It was something on which she was working in great detail. However, she had not made a report on it as yet, because—and she underlined the next phrase—*she did not report any work until it had been certainly demonstrated.*

As for the statistics amassed on cancer by the insurance

companies, Maud felt that they were of little help in settling the question. The present state of human statistics, at least regarding disease, were worse than useless in getting at the truth of the cancer-and-inheritance relationship. Too often, the statistics collected by the insurance companies were misleading. In view of this deplorable situation, the search for the truth had to take place in the laboratory, as done by her and Dr. Wood. The work had to be with lower animals. And there was no great disparity in her work and in Dr. Wood's. He used rats in his research, she used mice. But in fundamentals, Wood's research and her own more or less agreed, since nature was always consistent, even if man was not.

"May I not console you a little?" she wrote. She then said that Dr. C.'s thought that the inheritability of absolute immunity to cancer was a matter of "despair and gloom" was unfounded. The inheritability of absolute immunity to cancer was the most encouraging fact ever discovered about the disease. It meant that large numbers of individuals were wholly immune to cancer. Nothing could ever make the whole world immune, except the understanding and observance of the universal laws of heredity. "The sorrow arises out of the fact that we do not observe these laws," she added.

Maud asked Dr. C. to read this letter, as well as the one he sent to her, to the members of the Columbus Academy of Medicine. She enclosed a copy of the letter she had received from Francis Carter Wood, in which he had accused her of listening to "assorted gossip." She pointed out that Dr. Wood denied having any representatives who visited her laboratory. "Therefore," she said, "I could not have burst into tears in the presence of his representatives, as you reported to the physicians in Columbus." The incident never took place at all, she repeated, and the members of the Columbus Academy of Medicine should be so informed, and by him, the person who had brought the matter up in the first place.

However, Maud did not rely on Dr. C. to present her denial

to the Academy. She wrote to the Columbus physician who had first informed her of the charges made against her. She enclosed copies of Dr. Wood's letter and the last letter from Dr. C., requesting the friendly physician to read all of the letters to the members of the Columbus Academy of Medicine if Dr. C. did not.

Later, she was informed that this physician did bring the matter up before the Academy and asked Dr. C. for an apology to Maud. Dr. C. had refused and the matter was never resolved. However, the friendly physician assured Maud that he would continue to press for the apology he felt was due her.

Maud's insistence on the clearing of her name, coupled with the pressure from the friendly physician for a public apology to Maud, soon forced Dr. C. to do something to settle the matter. He did not make the apology. Instead, he wrote to Francis Carter Wood, enclosing copies of Maud's letters and the letter from Wood to Maud in which Wood denied making any statements about Maud Slye. Dr. C. asked Dr. Wood if the letter he had written to Maud Slye, or at least the copy Maud had sent to Dr. C., was accurate. Dr. C. told Wood that he had accepted his story about Maud and the "representatives" as an absolutely true fact, an incident that had actually taken place, but Maud Slye denied the whole thing. Dr. C. had a high regard for Dr. Wood, as well as confidence in the noted researcher's integrity and honesty of purpose. Therefore, Dr. C. was in a quandary about what it all meant, and could Dr. Wood set him straight?

Wood wrote to Dr. C. and informed him that the letter he, Wood, had sent to Maud Slye was "correctly reported by her." He thought the matter was getting too much attention and that it should end. He was too busy a man to be called on to straighten out the difficulties into which inaccurate reports of what he said or didn't say got someone into. Thus, Wood put the onus of the whole matter onto Dr. C.'s shoulders. Dr. C. found himself in the awkward position in which repeaters of gossip often land when one or more of the parties involved in the gossip categorically denies ever having created it. Since Wood denied originating the story, and no one else came forth to claim authorship, Dr. C. was stuck with it.

Dr. C. told Dr. Wood that he was very embarrassed over the remarks he had made about Maud Slye to the members of the Columbus Academy of Medicine. Wood wrote back that he should not be embarrassed. As for Maud's indignation over the affair, well, Dr. C. should not "take it to heart." Maud was always indignant with Dr. Wood.

Regarding the acceptance of Maud Slye's work, Wood told Dr. C. that the insurance companies paid no attention to the history of cancer in any human being. Even Maud's colleagues in zoology did not believe that she had proved her case. Wood said that he himself did not feel that Maud had proved that mouse cancer had exactly the same cause as human cancer. "When she does," said Wood, "she can talk."

The sorely perplexed Dr. C. wrote another letter to Maud, enclosing copies of the letters he had received from Francis Wood. He mentioned that he felt Wood had dodged the issue. He complained that his only sin was to repeat a statement he thought was true, since it came from the noted Dr. Wood, who now denied ever making it. Dr. C. now conceded that the distasteful episode, as represented, never did occur and that in repeating it to the member of the Columbus Academy of Medicine, he had done an injustice to Maud Slye. Therefore, he hoped she would accept his apology. Furthermore, he would make his apology before the Academy members at the first opportunity.

Maud now had Dr. C.'s apology and his promise to make it public. Finally, after months of accusations, charges, repudiations, and confusion, the matter was disposed of forever. At a later meeting of the Columbus Academy of Medicine, the members adopted the following resolution:

The Secretary is hereby directed to notify Dr. Maud Slye
that Dr. C. has read all the correspondence between Dr. F.
C. Wood, Dr. Maud Slye, and himself—including a letter
of apology to Dr. Slye.

At last, Maud's honor, integrity, and reputation were re-
stored.

Not too long after that, Maud received some more good
news, a welcome endorsement of her work. Dr. James Ewing,
the eminent pathologist and head of the Department of
Pathology at Cornell Medical College, issued a statement on
the significance of Maud Slye's work on the hereditary nature
of cancer. Ewing congratulated Maud on preparing statements about the inheritability of cancer that seemed to be
beyond "serious question." The recent statement made by
Maud about irritation as a cancer factor placed her in a much
stronger position. Ewing had been unable to assume that
heredity was the main factor in the origin of cancer, and he
had hoped that Maud would also admit that it was not. Now
that she had admitted that chronic irritation was also an
important factor in the incidence of cancer, he found her
doctrine more acceptable, including the possibility of
eliminating a recessive tendency to cancer by proper matings.
However, added Ewing, he was not sure about her statement
that the absence of the recessive character guarantees immunity to all forms of cancer. He felt the subject was too complex
for anyone to make that kind of statement.

What Ewing had written was a kind of white paper in which
he commented on a report by Maud Slye regarding the significance of her work on the hereditary nature of cancer. In general, he subscribed to all of Maud's statements regarding the
influence of heredity on the incidence of cancer in mice and
their probable application to cancer in human beings. He did
propose some limitations, but they did not seriously alter the
position taken by Maud Slye.

For one thing, Ewing questioned whether the natural life of the experimental animals exactly duplicated the conditions found in human society. He also wondered if all the tumors observed in lower animals covered all the various types of tumors found in human beings. He thought that Maud gave too much assurance to the absolute immunity of certain human beings when they were exposed to the necessary forms of irritation required to produce cancer. It was possible that immunity could be broken down during the relatively long life of a human being. The experimental data appeared to justify an intelligent selection in human mating for the purpose of avoiding cancer. (This was exactly what Maud had been saying for a long time.) This kind of selective mating, continued Ewing, would be extremely important in rural communities where intermarriage of cancer families was relatively common.

Ewing felt that in human beings there was a rather uniform susceptibility to certain major forms of cancer. So many factors entered into the causation of cancer that he hesitated to attribute to heredity alone all the responsibility for the appearance of cancer. The fact that the hereditary tendency to cancer was due to a recessive character, as Maud had demonstrated in her mice, and that it could be bred out was highly important, both from the genetic and the practical standpoints. Since scientists knew nothing about the original sources of the hereditary elements (this was before molecular biologists were able to reproduce the structure of DNA and to demonstrate its probable influence on heredity), the possibility remained that the hereditary tendency might develop spontaneously, through mutation. However, there was no experimental evidence of this fact. Ewing concluded his paper by congratulating Dr. Maud Slye on her very broad statements of the many phases of heredity in cancer, as "illuminated by her long researches."

Although the endorsement of her work by Dr. Ewing was a

qualified one, Maud was happy to receive it. Now she could turn to her manuscript of poetry and write:

So many roads that go!
My feet were set upon the service path,
Whose glory of the day is toil,
Whose peace at nightfall is the place of dreams
That reach beyond the stars!
Whose golden trumpet call
Is to the service of a higher toil;
O accolade of work folded away
And finished. It was for me to know the lonely feet,
The weary hands—but O the peace within my heart!

NINE

For more than twenty years, Maud had been working with her many generations of mice on the cancer-and-inheritance project. Gradually, more physicians and scientists were taking an objective look at her findings and conclusions. The endorsement of Maud's work by Professor Ewing, although qualified, had been of immense help to Maud. Because of Ewing's endorsement, other scientists were willing to consider her work instead of summarily dismissing it. However, there was still a hard core of physicians and researchers who not only refused to accept her conclusions, but ridiculed them.

Maud continued breeding her mice, producing spontaneous cancers in some strains and breeding cancer out of others. "The proof of the relation between heredity and the tendency to cancer immunity or susceptibility," she stated, "does not lie in securing the greatest possible number of cancers, but rather in establishing the fact that it is possible either deliberately to prevent or to occasion the occurrence of cancer by selective breeding—where every other possible factor is under complete control. In order to do this, it is necessary to have strains of animals analyzed as to their individual cancer potentialities, and that live well into cancer age without intercurrent infections."

In 1916, Maud had started a long-range mouse-breeding project that involved spontaneous thyroid tumors. She had undertaken this work to demonstrate whether or not heredity bore the same relation to the tendencies of resistance and susceptibility to thyroid tumors that it bore to tumors in other mouse organs. There were no other reports of any spontaneous thyroid tumors in mice. Moreover, very few malignant growths in the thyroid gland had been reported in other rodents. The few cases reported included five rats and one coypu, or nutria, a South American rodent. Thus, thyroid cancer was relatively rare in rodents, especially in mice. If Maud could breed a strain of mice that developed thyroid cancer, the occurrence of such cancer could not be attributed to chance. It was important that she avoid any chance occurrences of tumors, since her critics would pounce on them as further evidence that all the cancers in her mice were a result of chance or coincidence.

Maud used six unrelated stocks of Japanese waltzing mice for the study on thyroid cancer. The oldest of the six strains, which she designated as strain J. D. 1, originated from mice kept in the Yerkes Laboratory at Harvard University. During the fifteen years that Maud had been breeding this strain, no member had ever developed any kind of tumor, benign or malignant. A second stock of mice came from the laboratory animal market in Chicago and was labeled strain number J. D. 7. This strain was also free from tumors of any kind. Maud purchased the other four stocks of mice from four different sources in New Orleans. Two of these four stocks had never developed any tumors. The other two New Orleans stocks, J. D. 16–14 and J. D. 30–62–68, did produce tumors. Mice of the J. D. 16–14 strain developed mammary-gland tumors and mice of the strain J. D. 30–62–68 had malignant thyroid cancer.

This more or less negative evidence of cancer was important. Out of six stocks of Japanese waltzing mice, consisting of hundreds of individuals in the main line of the strain and derivatives handled by Maud Slye over a twenty-year period, four stocks showed complete exemption from tumors of any kind, even mammary-gland tumors, which were fairly common in mice. The fifth stock showed complete exemption from thyroid tumors, and the sixth stock, J. D. 30–62–68, showed complete exemption from all tumors *except those of the thyroid gland.*

When Maud studied the accumulated data on this mouse-breeding project, she realized that the results were striking and highly significant. Outside of her laboratory, there had been no reports of mouse strains producing thyroid tumors, either benign or malignant. Furthermore, the waltzing mice obtained in New Orleans had not, to anyone's knowledge, shown any signs of thyroid cancer. After the appearance of a thyroid tumor in one of the Japanese waltzers in Maud's laboratory, all of the stocks of waltzing mice were extensively bred to see if they would produce thyroid tumors. In five stocks, Maud found it impossible to produce even one tumor of the thyroid gland. In the sixth stock, J. D. 30–62–68, she was able to produce thyroid tumors in eleven mice. This sixth stock of mice was kept under conditions that were identical in every respect with those of the other five stocks.

The first thyroid tumor appeared in a male mouse, number 6219, a third-generation waltzer of stock number 30–62–68. This mouse died at the age of twelve months from chronic nephritis and coccidia, or protozoan parasite, infestation in the kidneys. He showed a malignant tumor of the thyroid gland that was mainly carcinomatous, with areas resembling sarcoma. Maud designated this tumor as sarcoma-carcinoma.

At the time, she had a very low budget for the thyroid cancer project and could keep only a small stock of Japanese waltzing mice. Therefore, although she had six different stocks of waltzing mice, the number of individuals in each strain was small. That had been her situation during the long years of research—a low budget that barely allowed her to do the work she wanted to do. She did not have the financial resources available to researchers at Harvard University or the Institute for Cancer Research at Columbia University.

Since her number of Japanese waltzing mice was small,

never exceeding fifty mice in each strain, Maud had to wait long periods of time for results. It took nearly two years for the next thyroid tumor to show up in a waltzer. When it did appear, it came in direct succession from mouse number 6219, the first mouse to develop a thyroid tumor. Just how many thyroid tumors might have been produced if the strain could have been bred out completely, Maud did not know. But five generations later, in generation eight of the strain itself, another sarcoma-carcinoma of the thyroid gland appeared in a female mouse, number 16917. These results caused Maud to believe that the tendency to resistance to cancer was definitely hereditary.

The next thyroid tumor in the genetic succession of strain 30–62–68 appeared in another female mouse, number 14959; the tumor was a bilateral sarcoma-carcinoma. Maud kept mouse number 14959 under constant care and observation for a four-month period, which ended with the death of the mouse. At the time of death, the mouse was nine and a half months old. She was the granddaughter of mouse number 16917. The two female mice, 16917 and 14959, had been kept in separage cages; therefore, their susceptibility to thyroid tumors was in no way due to contact.

Starting with the appearance of a thyroid tumor in mouse number 14959, Maud began a more intensive study of mouse strain 30–62–68. It seemed evident to her that the susceptibility to thyroid tumors was being carried in what she called Line II of the strain. Four tumors had appeared in a direct line. Therefore, Maud wanted to find out what Mendelian method of inheritance applied. Accordingly, female mouse 16917 was mated with a noncancerous male, number 13288, who died when he was about ten months old. None of the offspring resulting from this mating showed any tumors. Two of them died from intestinal infections when they were five months old. The others lived to be from seven to nine months of age. Resistance to thyroid carcinoma was dominant over susceptibility in this particular case, concluded Maud.

Maud had bred three pairs of hybrid mice and they produced offspring that formed lines I, II, and III of the strain. No
tumors of any kind ever appeared in lines I and III, even
though Maud still had these lines in her laboratory nearly
twenty years later. She felt that the results shown by these
lines were another corroboration of the inheritability of
cancer exemption, especially when exemption persisted in
the lines, or families, without a break for nearly twenty years.

Later, during Maud's experiments with the waltzers, she
mated a female mouse, number 17394, from generation eleven
of the strain with an unrelated male, number 13255. The
female was a hybrid carrier, daughter of mouse number
14959, which had developed a thyroid tumor. The male was a
member of a Japanese waltzing strain (J. D. 26–48) that was
wholly resistant to thyroid cancer, as well as to tumors in all
other organs. Consequently, no tumors appeared in the first
generation of hybrids that resulted from this mating, even
though some of its members lived to what was an advanced
age for Japanese waltzing mice: twenty to twenty-seven
months. By this mating and the ensuing offspring, Maud was
able to demonstrate once again the dominance of resistance
over susceptibility to thyroid cancer.

Next, Maud mated two individuals from the first-
generation hybrids produced by mouse number 17394 and
13255. One was a female that died when she was twenty
months old from chronic enteritis and a hypertrophied heart.
The other was a male that lived to be twenty-seven months
old, eventually succumbing to an unknown infection, but
without any cancer. Among the offspring of these two mice,
which were carriers of cancer susceptibility, was a female
mouse who died when she was thirteen months old of thyroid
carcinoma. Here again was evidence that showed the typical
Mendelian behavior of the tendencies to resistance and susceptibility to thyroid cancer.

In drawing up a résumé of mouse strain J. D. 30–62–68,
Maud found that she had some very interesting data. First, in

a relatively small family of 133 mice in a direct descent—mice that had been deliberately bred through twenty-eight generations to determine whether or not selective breeding could control the tendency to resistance and susceptibility to thyroid cancer — eleven malignant growths (or 8.2 percent of all deaths) appeared. The result demonstrated that susceptibility to malignant thyroid tumors was certainly carried in this particular strain of mice.

During the production of the twenty-eight generations of mice in strain 30–62–68, there had never been a tumor of any organ, either benign or malignant, in any direct or indirect line. The strain showed complete exemption from all neoplastic tendency except in the thyroid gland. In the first hybrid generation resulting from the mating of mice with thyroid cancer to cancer-resistant males there had been no signs of any cancer. This showed that resistance to thyroid cancer was dominant over the susceptibility to thyroid tumors.

But the mating of two first-generation hybrid carriers of malignant-thyroid-cancer susceptibility led to thyroid tumors in the next generation. Thus, the tendency to thyroid cancer was a true Mendelian recessive character. By the continued mating of mice resistant to thyroid cancer with hybrid carriers, Maud was able to hold off the occurrence of malignancy for as many generations as she wished. This experiment reemphasized the relation of heredity to resistance and susceptibility to thyroid cancer. It also reemphasized the dominance of resistance to cancer over susceptibility to cancer.

After holding off the occurrence of thyroid cancer for six generations, Maud was able to produce it again in successive generations. She did this by mating in each generation pure-breeding (homozygous) resistant individuals with what apparently were hybrid carriers, and then interbreeding the hybrids of the next generation. By these matings, she showed that the hereditary potentiality had been carried through the preceding six generations.

This experiment showed beyond a doubt the relation of heredity to the occurrence of resistance and susceptibility to thyroid cancer. It was in complete harmony with the results shown in all other tests of all other types and locations of tumors in mice in Maud's laboratory over an eighteen-year period. She had conducted this study on thyroid tumors under controlled conditions. Her Japanese waltzing mice were treated equally in every detail of their handling and all the outside environmental influences that might have affected them.

Japanese waltzing mice are extremely delicate and hyper-sensitive to all kinds of infections. Therefore, to protect them, Maud kept the waltzers in wooden boxes that were 12 by 6 by 6 inches in size. Each box had a firmly fitting cover of wire mesh. The mice were sheltered from drafts, but had access to light and air by way of the wire-mesh lids. All of the Japanese waltzers were kept in the same room in the southwest corner of Maud's laboratory, an area of the building that received sunlight from the south and west. All of the mouse boxes were placed so they would receive the maximum sunlight at some period of the day, when there was any sunshine, and no mouse family had any advantage or disadvantage when it came to environmental conditions.

Maud was extremely careful and scrupulous in the matter of sanitation. She knew the Japanese waltzers were sensitive to infections, and she spared no effort in the housekeeping of the delicate mice. All of the mice used in the thyroid-cancer experiments were under Maud's personal observation on a daily basis. She handled each mouse. They were moved into clean, sterilized boxes twice a week. All equipment was thoroughly cleaned and sterilized before being put back into a mouse box. Water for the mice was boiled and filtered and then placed in sterile containers. The diet of the waltzers consisted of thoroughly toasted fresh bread, well moistened with doubly pasteurized whole milk, mixed with birdseed (millet, hemp, and canary seed), and timothy hay free from mold. No Japanese waltzer in the experiment ever received any other kind of food, nor did Maud vary the feeding routine for any mouse or group of mice. She personally fed and watered the mice, and all of them were fed and watered from the same general supply each day. No factor in the placing of the mouse boxes or in the diet, water, sanitation, or handling of the mice could have affected the incidence of cancer or any other disease.

The results of Maud's long experiment with thyroid cancer in the Japanese waltzing mice conflicted with the conclusions of several cancer researchers, among whom was a scientist named Burrows. Burrows disregarded heredity as a causative factor in the incidence of cancer. His theory of the cause of cancer was based on the presence or absence of certain vitamins. In his opinion, the presence of what he called the "archusia," or growth factor, which he identified with vitamin B, and the absence of what he termed the "ergusia," or growth-inhibiting factor, which he identified as vitamin A, were the direct and universal causes of cancer. Burrow's conclusions were based upon studies of cancer growing *in vitro*, or in test tubes.

Maud had handled about 75,000 mice in her laboratory over a twenty-year period. All of the mice were fed diets that were identical in every item, with the exception of a relatively few mice that were involved in nutrition experiments. Out of the 75,000 mice in her laboratory, eleven had developed thyroid cancer; more than 74,900 mice had had no thyroid tumors. Of the 74,900 mice, only six had ever shown even simple enlargement of the thyroid gland. In view of these data, Maud found it difficult to see what role vitamins A and B played as causative factors. She concluded that whatever role vitamins A and B played in the incidence of cancer, it was not the exclusive role assigned to them by Burrows.

The only role that the vitamins might play, in Maud's opinion, would be in a special situation where a mouse could not utilize the two vitamins in the right proportion, even though the vitamins were fed to the mouse in sufficient quantities. However, the inability to utilize the vitamins would have to be entirely local, since hundreds of mice in Maud's laboratory afflicted with breast cancer and other malignant tumors bore several litters of young that were normal in every way. Furthermore, the young were suckled to normal development. Maud believed this indicated that all functions in the mother were going on normally, even the function of normal secretion in those mammary tissues not involved in breast cancers.

Maud also thought that the inability to utilize vitamins A and B would have to be at indefinite age occurrences, since cancer occurred in her stock of mice from age twelve days to five years. The inability to utilize the vitamins could not be evident at birth, because no mouse in Maud's laboratory had ever had cancer at birth. Therefore, in order for Burrows' theory to make sense, according to Maud, certain conditions had to be met. And chief among them was that there would have to be a sharply localized inability to utilize vitamins A and B in the right proportion. Such inability would be likely to arise at any age from twelve days to five years from an entirely undetermined cause. That unknown cause was resident in the constitution of the mouse, but it was not seen at birth. It could not affect breast secretions, even when a mouse had a well-developed breast tumor. She thought that this was a most unreasonable assumption.

In a paper published in the *Journal of Cancer Research*, Burrows had written:

Cancer is a disease which must be prevalent in an undernourished race and one which suffers from substances and conditions capable of removing vitamin A from their tissues. It must disappear when the nutrition of this race is improved—they cease to be slaves of fashion—have protected themselves against improper drugs—abuses of certain trades—and freed themselves from diseases such as syphilis, which causes undernutrition.

Maud disagreed with the conclusions of Burrows. None of what he said applied in any degree to the appearance of more than five thousand spontaneous tumors in the mice in her laboratory. She pointed out that in her laboratory the mice that developed tumors were the largest and most perfect specimens. They were not undernourished, nor were they the victims of the abuses that Burrows said led to cancer. Maud's mice performed all of their normal functions, including the bearing and suckling of normal offspring; they also had a normal lifespan and normal reproduction potency.

She stated that no evidence existed to warrant the assumption of a complete analogy between tissue cultures of cancer (that is, cancers grown by Burrows in test tubes) and spontaneous tumors arising and developing in a living organism (as in Maud's mice), all of whose functions were completely and vitally interrelated. This complex interrelationship had to be taken into account in any theory of the nature of cancer. The controlling influence of heredity in determining the occurrence, type, and location of tumors was indisputably proved by Maud's study of thyroid cancer in mice. Moreover, this fact had to be considered in any theory as to the cause of cancer and the stimulus for its growth.

Maud was convinced that her experiments with the Japanese waltzing mice and thyroid cancer reinforced her conclusions on the relationship between cancer and heredity. She had found no links between the age of her mice, the conditions under which they were kept, or their routine care, and the development of thyroid tumors. The facts compiled from her research were obtained by adhering to the classic requirements for a scientific experiment. All of the thyroid cancers in her mice came from one strain of Japanese waltzing mice. In hundreds of other strains of mice raised in her laboratory, involving about seventy-five thousand mice, there had been only six simple enlargements of the thyroid gland. And no case of thyroid tumors in a mouse had been reported from any other laboratory. Therefore, reasoned Maud, it was impossible to deny the influence of heredity in determining the occurrence of thyroid cancers, especially after the careful control with which her study had been carried out.

Maud reiterated what she had said many times before. There were two factors necessary for the occurrence of cancer: a hereditary predisposition to cancer and chronic irritation or trauma of the appropriate kind and degree applied to cancer-susceptible tissues. She admitted that it was difficult to demonstrate all possible factors, since complete biologic control was nearly impossible.

In view of the fact that irritation was a factor in the development of cancer, Maud urged that more careful studies of this factor be undertaken. All such studies would have to be carried out with animals that were analyzed as to their cancer potentiality, so that the hereditary factor could be carefully controlled. With analyzed animals and the selection of animals whose hereditary tendencies were appropriate to the test, it would then be possible to find out what caused cancer. And she was already at work in this area.

TEN

A number of researchers continued to challenge Maud Slye's conclusions about the inheritability of cancer, specifically her belief that susceptibility to it was due to a simple Mendelian recessive character. One of them was Dr. Clarence Cook Little, who had several times in the past criticized Maud's conclusions, as well as her methods of research. Little had conducted experiments on grafted tumors in mice and had made many studies on inheritance. His papers and reports had appeared in the medical and scientific journals. At the time that Maud published her work on thyroid tumors in Japanese waltzing mice, he was the president of the University of Michigan.

Dr. Little was one of the country's leading researchers. He had earned his A.B. degree in 1910 at Harvard University. He remained at Harvard to earn an M.S. degree in 1912 and a D.Sc. degree in zoology in 1914. His main interest had been in the field of genetics, and he had conducted various inheritance experiments while at Harvard. His first scientific paper, *The Peculiar Inheritance of Pink Eyes Among Colored Mice*, had been published in 1909, and had called attention to this promising geneticist and zoologist.

In 1924, Little had become the youngest president of the University of Michigan. However, his career was recorded as "brilliant but tactless," because he had a way of getting through red tape and challenging long-established dicta that often brought him into collision with more cautious members of the faculty staff. Nevertheless, Little had productive years at the University, during which he produced thirty-six scientific papers.

The subjects of Little's papers showed the broad range of his interests. He wrote about coat-color inheritance in mice; human sex ratios; coat-color inheritance in Great Danes, in doves, and in canaries; tests for psychological differences in transplanted tumors; chromosomes in fruit flies; the relationships between research in human heredity and experimental genetics; the effects of X rays on mice; medical education; the training of college and university teachers; and a subject that was to occupy him for the rest of his life: cancer.

Clarence Cook Little, in the opinion of many scientists, was eminently qualified to pass judgment on the work and conclusions of Maud Slye. And he had done so. His first criticism was a short article in *Science* in which he stated that Maud had committed an error in the genetic interpretation of her experiments with albinism in one of her early mouse studies. At the time, he had commented that the error was important enough to cast reasonable doubt on the "soundness" of her genetic training and background. Although he had thought it pointless to belabor the error in interpreting coat-color inheritance, the fact that Maud Slye was conducting research in cancer made it necessary to point out the error. Too many false hopes had been built up and later destroyed in cancer investigations. Therefore, Little had reasoned, it was wrong to allow even a simple but incorrect genetic interpretation to go unchallenged, especially when the proponent had not supported it with adequate data.

Little made it known that Maud Slye was not the first scientist to demonstrate that certain forms of cancer were hereditary in mice. "The fact that the tendency to certain forms of cancer is hereditary in mice has been established for some years," he stated. He referred to the work of Tyzzer in 1909 and the experiments of Murray in 1911 as examples of investigations into cancer and inheritance prior to the work of Maud Slye. But Little was forced to admit that no series of studies on cancer and heredity had done more to influence gradually the opinion of the medical profession than the twenty-six reports published over a fifteen-year period by Maud Slye, Gideon Wells, and Harriet Holmes.

However, Dr. Little stoutly maintained that Maud's research, supported by Gideon Wells of the Sprague Memorial Institute, contained too many errors of interpretation, and that the medical profession was wrongly influenced by her work and conclusions. He pointed out that Maud's work had a number of examples of incorrectly explained results and that therefore there was a need to revise "the dogmatic and absolute assertion made by Slye [and supported by Wells] whose absence of genetic knowledge should have at least produced caution."

Little was again attacking Maud's competence as a geneticist. The "dogmatic assertion" that he referred to had been made in one of Maud's papers, "The Inheritance Behavior of Cancer as a Simple Mendelian Recessive" (Report Number 21). The statement Maud made was this: "The conclusions published have been based upon over five thousand primary spontaneous neoplasms, including nearly every type known in human pathology. In every one of these five thousand neoplasms, both external and internal, the inheritance behavior of cancer susceptibility has been that of a simple Mendelian recessive."

Dr. Little refused to accept this conclusion. He claimed that Maud's own published data disproved her Mendelian recessive theory. He thought it was regrettable that she persisted in such an erroneous interpretation of her own data and called on the members of the American Association for Cancer Research to review the facts and draw their own conclusions.

Little proceeded to pinpoint what he called Maud's "errors of interpretation" in her research and questioned her methods as well. He accused her of giving a false impression of the genetic data of almost 700 matings listed in one of her reports. What Maud had done, according to Little, was to reprint or use certain matings in more than one report, thus making it appear as though more matings had taken place. He added that "a rough count shows at least 11 matings published twice in different reports, 29 matings three times, 14 matings four times, 6 matings five times, 1 mating six times, and 1 mating nine times." He concluded this piece of criticism by saying that Maud should have stated that her tabulations involving 5,000 neoplasms actually involved only 530 neoplasms.

"One of the first matters of interest as a test of whether cancer is a simple recessive," wrote Dr. Little in the *Journal of Cancer Research*, "is found in a tabulation of the results of cancer mated with cancer [that is, cancerous mice mated with cancerous mice] as given by Slye." He included the following table in his critique:

Number of matings	Progeny cancerous	Progeny noncancerous
106	241	106
[106]	347*	0*

*results to be expected according to Maud Slye's hypothesis

These figures, in Dr. Little's opinion, were obviously so out of agreement with Maud's hypothesis that he believed further study aimed at a more correct explanation was in order. He also thought that in the matings given by Maud, noncancerous animals, both of whose parents were cancerous, should have been included in the tabulations. This was necessary because if cancer was due to a simple recessive character, then all descendents of any two cancerous mice mated with each other were genetically cancerous regardless of their physical appearance.

But Little argued that the susceptibility to cancer was not due to a simple Mendelian recessive character. He thought it would be strange if all forms of cancer were genetically alike and that they could be described as constituting together a simple Mendelian recessive character, as Maud Slye maintained. A direct and satisfactory test could be applied. If all types of cancer other than those of the mammary gland were genetically similar, then the crossmating of a mouse with cancer of the lung and one with sarcoma of the liver should produce just as many cancerous offspring as would a mating between parents both of which had cancer of the lungs. In other words, if cancer susceptibility was due to a simple Mendelian recessive character, dissimilar types of cancer in the parents should make no difference in the incidence of cancer in the offspring. If cancer was a simple recessive character, both types of mating should give 100 percent cancerous young.

On the other hand, if cancer of the liver was genetically different from cancer of the lung, or if sarcoma of the face was genetically different from cancer of the liver, then, according to Little, it could be expected that dissimilar cancerous parents would give a high proportion of noncancerous young, whereas similar cancerous parents would not.

What Little was talking about here is a general principle well known to geneticists. It involves complementary genes. These are two or more genes whose combined effect is qualitatively different from the separate effect of any one of them.

The test between similar and dissimilar matings was a simple one. Little pointed out that Maud's own data had a bearing on the principle and provided definite evidence of it, as exemplified in this table:

	Progeny	
	Non-cancerous	Can-cerous
Parents alike as to type of cancer	0	27
Parents different as regards type of cancer	28	15

The figures given by Maud Slye in this table were so obvious as to present a self-evident difference between the matings. The conclusions to be drawn were that (1) the matings of unlike cancerous parents produced many more noncancerous individuals than did the matings of parents with similar types of cancer, (2) the results of Maud's test showed definitely that the two types of matings were genetically dissimilar, and (3) different types of cancer were dependent upon different genes. And Dr. Little quickly pointed out that this proved strikingly that cancer as a whole did not behave like a simple Mendelian recessive character, such as albinism.

Dr. Little gave Maud credit for having made a very extensive series of observations. She had conducted autopsies on thousands of mice, and her overall project was one of considerable magnitude. Maud had used the diagnosis of the cause of death of each mouse as a very important part of her records on the matings of mice. Little could not help making the point that in the case of laboratory mice, infectious diseases, about which researchers knew very little, could be the cause of some inaccuracies in Maud's diagnoses or even her judgment. However, even if this were the case, commented Little, Maud Slye's efforts were highly commendable.

In her report, Maud had attributed the death of one mouse to "senile atrophy." Dr. Little questioned the validity of this diagnosis, even as a contributory cause of death in a mouse whose age had been given as seven months. How could a mouse seven months old be considered senile?

Little singled out what he considered to be another glaring error in Maud's report. This involved mouse number 5418 (male). In one paper, Maud had reported this mouse as having been descended from female mouse number 3768 and male mouse number 4933; yet, in another paper, she had listed this mouse as having descended from female mouse number 4730 and male mouse number 4310. Dr. Little, in a charitable statement about this mixup, stated, "This probably is a case of typographical error in chart making, but it is apt to lead to considerable confusion."

These apparent errors led Dr. Little to view Maud's data with suspicion. He warned that in such important subjects as genetics and cancer, it was imperative to proceed with great caution both in the collection and in the graphic presentation of data and in the theoretical interpretation of observed phenomena. Besides the scientific difficulties in the study of the genetics of cancer, there was an obligation of a more or less social nature. This obligation involved a responsibility for extreme caution in the interpretation of results in order that no false hopes would be raised. Cancer was unquestionably a scourge of humanity, said Dr. Little. If a new method of analysis or a new approach was advertised as having produced simple and startling results, it was necessary for some time to elapse before the medical profession could adopt the new interpretation. At first, naturally, the profession must be cautious and suspicious. That had been the case in the reported experimental work on the genetics of cancer. After a time, however, because of repeated positive statements by Maud Slye and Gideon Wells—and few, if any, expressed dissenting opinions—the view that all forms of cancer were due to a single and simple Mendelian recessive character had become widespread and favorably received.

Dr. Little thought that the acceptance of Maud Slye's hypothesis was most unfortunate. But since it had been accepted by a number of physicians and scientists, disillusionment was bound to occur if results were questioned. For that reason he was not trying to discredit her observations but was merely calling attention to the apparent errors in her work. What he wanted to emphasize was that the simplicity and dogmatism of Maud's genetic interpretation was misleading and in need of immediate positive denial and correction.

Unfortunately, in Dr. Little's opinion, the methods used by Maud Slye to tabulate or analyze her data were not conducive to creating an opportunity for other scientists to observe contrasts. He thought that by publishing detailed pedigrees of her individual mice and families, Maud had found an excellent way to bring out the results of any one particular mating. However, it did not provide the grouped data that helped a scientist observe and record general differences, such as those on which the correctness of the application of Mendel's Law would largely depend.

The mating of two cancerous mice by Maud Slye that showed 100 percent noncancerous offspring proved that the tests made—regardless of how numerous—were not all-conclusive. If the exceptions were said to be mice that had died before cancer age, Maud had not showed this in her tabulations. Moreover, continued Little in his critique, she had not presented extensive tables or curves to show the range of age at which cancer occurred in the various strains or families of mice in succeeding generations. The work of many other investigators had repeatedly shown that this was an important factor and could not be safely ignored. Also, if the question of "cancer age" was to be considered, one must keep in mind its application to the lines or families classed as "noncancerous." If, as in at least one case cited by Maud Slye, "senile atrophy" was listed as a cause of death, then there should have been some mice that had the potential of developing tumors at a very early age. Finally, in connection with pedigrees, Maud should have recorded the relation of these mice to strains whose age incidence was somewhat near that which was usual in mice.

Little took up the matter of irritation as a factor in cancer incidence. He thought that the general treatment of irritation in relation to cancer also needed careful analysis in connection with Maud's general data. The question posed was whether internal imbalance and the irritating effects of natural degeneration were not contributing factors in every case of cancer. He maintained that it would be oversimplifying, as well as superficial, to consider irritation *only* or even *chiefly* in those cases in which obvious trauma was involved.

Apropos of this matter, there were, in the matings of cancerous mice described by Maud Slye, twelve males that had been recorded as having died from wounds and one mouse that had died from a sarcoma of the testicle. The latter condition might have been caused, at least in part, by wounds received in fighting, since male mice try to castrate male rivals. That twelve potentially cancerous mice and, according to Maud Slye, genetically cancerous mice, had died from wounds without developing tumors showed that heredity and irritation in their cases were not sufficient to cause neoplasia, concluded Little. They were not easily explained on the supposition that cancer was due to a simple Mendelian recessive character. On the other hand, if cancer was not a simple Mendelian recessive character, the presence of what otherwise were exceptions would be quite understandable.

However, Little conceded the various tests and tabulations of Maud Slye's data certainly justified the conclusions of earlier investigators—namely, that hereditary predisposition played an important role in the incidence of cancer. Other investigators, including himself, had been aware of that general fact before Maud Slye published her reports. But he agreed that scientists were now able to do more toward analyzing the nature of the inheritance process in its relation to cancer because of her published data.

After this begrudging compliment, Little reminded scientists that Maud's data showed that the genetic behavior of mammary-gland cancer was quite different and distinct from that of other types of cancer. But she had not shown how mammary-gland cancer was different. Little said that the chief difference between mammary-gland cancer and other types of cancer was that it was sex-linked and due to a *dominant* character, a fact supported by the work of other researchers.

Little further believed that the nonmammary types of cancer, as recorded by Maud Slye, gave clear evidence that more than one genetic factor was involved. This conclusion was supported by the relatively low percentage of cancerous progeny obtained when parents with different types of cancer were mated and by the high proportion obtained when similar cancer types were bred together. The complicated nature of cancer, its menace to the human species, and the need for increasing the confidence of the medical profession in genetic methods of analysis justified the definite decision at this time to publicize that all forms of cancer in mice were not due to a single and simple Mendelian recessive character, as postulated by Maud Slye. Little felt that a continued study, with more careful genetic analysis than that given by Maud Slye up to then, should precede any further development of her data from a genetic point of view.

This highly critical and authoritative paper on Maud Slye's work and conclusions caused quite a commotion in the cancer-research field. Those physicians and scientists who had accepted Maud's work now had some doubts about her conclusions, particularly since they had been challenged and refuted by Clarence Cook Little, who was highly qualified to criticize Maud's conclusions. Consequently, she found herself in the position of either having to admit that she had made some vital errors in her interpretation of her data or to say that Clarence Cook Little was in error. Either way, Little's criticism was the most thorough attack on Maud's work so far, and it was by far the strongest challenge she had received in all her long years of research. It was a challenge she dared not ignore.

ELEVEN

After Clarence Cook Little had done such a thorough job of critically analyzing Maud Slye's research methods and conclusions, Maud was forced into a defensive position more tenuous than that caused by any previous criticism. Many scientists were now agreeing with Little's analysis of her work, and they seemed inclined to accept his conclusions on the hereditary nature of cancer. A few physicians and scientists adopted a more cautious attitude in the controversy, letting Dr. Little and other prominent researchers carry on the arguments as to the validity and merit of Maud Slye's research.

The press, mainly the medical and scientific reporters, played up the controversy going on within the scientific community regarding cancer and heredity. Some reporters presented the controversy as a feud between Maud Slye and Clarence Cook Little, two researchers who had divergent views on the relationship between cancer and heredity. Though the cancer-and-heredity controversy was not featured on the front pages of the major newspapers, the subject was important enough to merit coverage, at least in the usual science and medicine sections of metropolitan newspapers.

However, not all the newspaper stories about Maud Slye and her research were accurate. *The New York Sun* ran the following item:

DECLARES CANCER NOT GERM DISEASE
Prof. Maud Slye Also Says It Is
Not Contagious

After sixteen years of study and experimentation, during which she used 50,000 mice, Prof. Maud Slye of the University of Chicago is convinced that cancer is hereditary and that it is not a germ disease. The disease is not contagious, as her experiments show, she says.

Professor Slye started her experiments in 1900 with two mice. She grafted a bit of tumerous growth into the bodies of mice and found that the offspring inherited the disease.

In an effort to prove her theory that the disease is not of germ origin, Prof. Slye many times has placed perfectly healthy mice in the same cages with diseased ones. Instead of contracting the disease by propinquity, the mice remained healthy, she said. This, she said, proves that cancer is not a germ disease.

"Apparently two factors are necessary to produce cancer. One is the inherited susceptibility and the other is irritation of the right kind applied to cancer susceptible tissues," she said.

Maud deplored this kind of reporting on her work, especially since it contained some inaccurate statements, the most glaring of which was the statement that she had grafted a bit of tumorous growth into the bodies of her mice. She had never grafted any tumors into any of her mice. All of the cancers developed by her mice were spontaneous cancers, that appeared in a natural way and not by grafting. Inaccurate newspaper items and articles only added to her difficulties and confused the public.

As for Dr. Little's devastating criticism of her work in the *Journal of Cancer Research*, Maud realized that she would have to respond to it. Regardless of Little's reputation as a cancer researcher, Maud felt that his attack on her was both contemptuous and unprofessional, and she could not let it go uncontested.

The cancer controversy was not a simple one; no easy explanations or even guidelines existed. Cancer research, whether on animals or human beings, involved long studies, which were made very difficult by several factors. First of all, cancer was a disease of middle and late life in human beings. Many potentially cancerous individuals died from other causes before they showed any signs of cancer. Thus, researchers were blocked in their efforts to obtain continuous data.

Next was the matter of irritation being a causative factor in cancer incidence. Maud had never denied that irritation or lesions, gross or microscopic, were involved in the causation of cancer. What her years of experimentation with mice had revealed was that any irritation was usually added to hereditary susceptibility when cancer did occur in her mice. Individuals susceptible by heredity might never encounter the type of irritation or lesions favorable for the inducement of cancer in the locally susceptible tissues. This fact could account for the low incidence of breast cancer in males. Maud pointed out that the conservative estimate of breast cancer in human males was about 1 percent of all breast cancer occurrences. Therefore, she stated in rebuttal to Dr. Little's assertion, breast-cancer susceptibility could not be sex-limited.

A more logical explanation was that male breast tissues were less subject to lesions than those of females. This would account for the less frequent incidence of breast tumors in males. The fact that susceptible tissues might never encounter the type of irritation or lesions necessary to induce cancer could result in a loss of valuable data. Also, Maud found that her male mice with breast cancer transmitted it just as surely as did females with breast tumors.

Of major importance, regarding long studies, was that research budgets (at least hers) simply did not allow for the complete breeding out of all experimental animals. Because of this restriction, valuable data could be lost. In the matter of low research budgets, Maud could speak from personal experience. She operated on a very low budget and used some of her own small salary to help defray expenses, all of which made it very difficult for her.

Another problem in cancer research was that individuals potentially cancerous or noncancerous might die *in utero* (in the womb) or might never reach existence because the ova remain unfertilized. One of Dr. Little's assumptions was that homozygous cancer was lethal. Maud said that he had made no allowance for noncancerous individuals who for one reason or another were never born. Here again, she argued, was a situation that caused a loss of important data.

Finally, other intercurrent pathological conditions or possibly even nutrition or some other cause could prevent the development of cancer in susceptible individuals, causing the loss of valuable data. Any researcher investigating the relationship between cancer and heredity had to contend with these factors or obstacles. Maud thought they were potent enough, given the present state of cancer research, to make it impossible for her, or for anyone else, to study the subject completely. She believed that the obstacles were so complicated that if they were rigidly applied to any theory of heredity in cancer, the evidence would never be complete in every detail.

In his critique, Dr. Little had questioned a number of cases that Maud had reported in her numerous papers. He thought she erred in not including in her charts and records those mice that had not shown signs of cancer at necropsy, but which might have developed tumors had they lived. Maud said that Little was assuming too much and that the best she, or any other researcher, could do was to include only those animals that showed cancer at necropsy. If, said Maud, it was assumed, as Dr. Little assumed in his discussion of matings between cancerous mice, that the offspring of double cancerous parentage had to be potentially cancerous, and they were recorded as such, then scientists might assume whatever they were trying to prove.

Whatever the interpretation of the genetic factor in cancer might turn out to be, continued Maud, the rule of classifying only those animals that actually showed demonstrable cancer at necropsy must be rigidly applied in every cancer researcher's work. Unless this was done, researchers could make whatever assumptions fitted their own particular theories and could omit others as, she pointed out, Dr. Little had apparently done in his criticism of her work. The rule had to be followed without deviation, whether a scientist agreed with Dr. Little that cancer of the breast was a sex-linked, dominant character (meaning the gene is carried on the sex chromosome) or whether he or she believed it was due to a simple recessive character. Maud asserted that each researcher had to stand the loss in figures that might help his or her theory, but that loss was surely better than an assumption.

Maud disagreed with Dr. Little's statement that the genetic factor in cancer was a heterozygous dominant character. She also objected to his statement that "the hypothesis that the heterozygous mammary cancer type is lethal fits the observed figures most closely." She said this was pure assumption on Little's part. There was no evidence to support it. As far as she was concerned, the statement appeared to be a handy device to make Little's theory more tenable.

On the other hand, her theory that the genetic factor in cancer was a recessive character had been fully established after the complete analysis of three strains of mice. It was with these three strains of mice that Dr. Little took issue, stating that Maud had given the impression that she had done more crossbreeding than had actually taken place in her laboratory. Maud replied that she never intended to give a false impression as to her crossbreeding in the three strains of mice. It was simply a question of budgetary limitations and of the limited life of the researcher, which made it impossible to analyze every strain of mice and every individual within a strain. In fact, Maud's published analysis of her mouse strains was the only published record available.

In her judgment, one series of charts (such as her charts on mouse strains), with each mouse genetically and pathologically analyzed, was of more value than tons of unanalyzed tables or records in determining the nature of a genetic factor. What did actually happen must represent the facts, and that was on the charts of the three mouse strains on which Maud had based her interpretation of the genetic factor in cancer susceptibility and cancer resistance. There was no item in all of the cancer incidence and in the behavior of cancer ever noted in her laboratory that did not go along with this interpretation. Therefore, her statement that all of the results obtained in her studies were consistent with the theory that cancer susceptibility was the result of a Mendelian recessive character still stood, as far as she was concerned.

Maud's chart on mouse strain 145 showed the mating between an extracted (produced by controlled breeding) cancerous male (274) with primary carcinoma of the lung, with a female (168) that died from uncertain causes. The female's mother, mouse 499, had died from chronic nephritis but without any cancer, and the father, mouse number 250, had died from pulmonary infection but without any cancer. Therefore, female mouse number 168 appeared to have been a purebred noncancerous mouse. Both parents of male mouse 274 had carcinoma of the lung; the mother, mouse number 158, had mammary tumors, which had spread to the lungs, and the father, mouse 193, had a primary carcinoma of the lung. Male mouse 274 therefore appeared to be a purebred cancerous mouse with no "sex-limited" type of neoplasm.

The first hybrid generation resulting from this mating showed no cancer. All of the offspring (six females, two males), lived to cancer age. If, as Dr. Little claimed, cancer were a dominant character, either simple or complex, either sex-limited or not sex-limited, then four, and possibly all eight, of the offspring in the first generation of this particular mouse family would have been cancerous. But none had appeared. Furthermore, said Maud, nobody could claim that lung cancer was sex-limited, because it occurred in both sexes. If the male was homozygous for cancer, then there should have been a 100-percent incidence of cancer in the first hybrid generation from mating lung-cancer male mouse 274 with noncancerous female mouse number 168. Even if he was heterozygous, there should have been a 50-percent incidence of cancer in the first generation. Instead, there had been none.

Dr. Little's attempt to separate the genetic factor in breast cancer from the genetic factor in other types and locations of tumors had been, in Maud's opinion, a bit premature. There was insufficient evidence to warrant such an assumption. Maud cited the case of male mouse 274, which had had a primary carcinoma of the lung and no breast cancer; this mouse had transmitted the breast-cancer tendency of his mother (mouse number 158) to his offspring in the mating with female mouse 168, a noncancerous mouse. Although breast cancer did not appear in the first generation resulting from this mating, it did appear in the next or second generation when two of the first-generation hybrids were mated. Three out of the twelve second-generation mice (two females and one male) developed cancer. Maud pointed out that this result was the exact 25-percent expectation for a simple Mendelian recessive character.

This kind of evidence seemed to link very closely the genetic behavior of different types and locations of malignancies. Maud considered it unwise—at least at the present time—to try to draw conclusions that various types and locations of malignancies were controlled by different genetic factors, as Little postulated, at least until the evidence was all in. What evidence there was on hand indicated the reverse of what Dr. Little had concluded.

Maud's results with cancerous and noncancerous mice, which had been obtained during many years of crossbreeding and analysis of mice, ruled out the theory that the genetic factor in cancer susceptibility was a dominant character, either simple or complex. Her long experiments had also demonstrated that cancer susceptibility was not sex-limited or heterozygous dominant. No cancer had appeared in the first hybrid generation of any crossmating between a cancerous and a purebred noncancerous mouse. But cancer had occurred in 25 percent of the offspring in the second hybrid generation just as a Mendelian recessive character would be expected to appear.

The important point was that Maud's charts were conclusive because they were made up of mice that had been genetically and pathologically analyzed by her. All possible types of genetic factors for cancer had been considered in studying the results of her experiments, and only the conclusion that cancer susceptibility was due to a simple recessive character seemed tenable to Maud. The behavior of the cancer-inheritance factor as shown in her charts could not be explained by Dr. Little's theory. In fact, said Maud, it completely nullified his theory.

Even Dr. Little's work with grafted tumors, which Maud claimed produced nothing comparable to work with spontaneous tumors, was shaky as far as proving cancer susceptibility was concerned. Little had stated, on the basis of his grafted tumors, that the genetic factor in spontaneous cancer was complex, with a dominant character prevailing. He further stated that he had achieved 100 percent "takes" in the first hybrid generation. This percentage was what he had taken as the basis for his theory, adding that there was a decreasing occurrence of cancer in later generations.

Maud believed, however, that this appearance of cancer in

the second generation might have occurred from an altered technique in grafting the tumors into the mice. Also, at the time that Little had done his cancer-grafting work, he had made no mention of his cancerous mice's being the heterozygous type.

"By adopting his new theory of cancer as heterozygous dominant," said Maud, "Dr. Little placed himself where he must either admit that grafted tumors are wholly unlike spontaneous tumors, and that genetic work with grafted tumors has no bearing upon the question of the relation of heredity to human cancer or any other spontaneous cancer—or he must admit that there are homozygous cancers." She also said that Little's claim that in his work with grafted tumors he had achieved 100 percent of cancer "takes" in the first generation required a closer look. The percentage of "takes" claimed by Little would have been possible under his theory only if he had supposed cancer to be a homozygous dominant character.

Even Dr. Little should have seen the necessity to clear a pathway through this rather chaotic combination of opinions, declared Maud. If the tendency to cancer grafts that took hold was due to a heterozygous dominant character, as Little's latest theory postulated, then he could have had only 50 percent of cancer "takes," instead of the 100 percent he claimed. In line with this reasoning, Maud felt that Little had to discard one or the other of his two contradictory theories—that is, either that grafted cancers were different from spontaneous cancers, or that there were homozygous cancers.

As far as Maud was concerned, Little's theory that the genetic factor in cancer susceptibility was due to a dominant character, either homozygous or heterozygous, had been demonstrated to be impossible by her long research.

Little's allegation that Maud had misled her readers into thinking more thyroid tumors had developed in her mice than had actually occurred particularly irked her. She answered this charge, saying,

Had such a purpose inspired me, it would have been defeated by the discussion in the article, which plainly states that there were eleven of these malignancies in a family of 133 members. Is it necessary to state that the article was not intended for casual reading? However, even the casual reader would, I think, have saved himself the trouble of reading the entire article and studying the charts with the stars [asterisks], and would read the summary. Here he would find the definite statement that there were eleven of these tumors in a family of 133 members, thus furnishing the highest record of thyroid malignancy anywhere reported in any species, or 8.2 percent of all deaths at all ages. All of the charts are impossible of explanation by the theory of cancer as a dominant character. They are nearly perfect for cancer recessive.

Maud also took exception to Dr. Little's minor complaints about her work and reports. To begin with, Maud had never claimed to be the first researcher to conduct experiments on the possible genetic linkage between cancer and heredity, as Dr. Little had implied in his criticism. In all of her articles and reports, she had listed all other researchers engaged in studying the relationship between cancer and inheritance. She had also acknowledged the value of the work done in this field as it had related to her own research on cancer and heredity.

Maud remarked that Dr. Little seemed to take a delight in pointing out that she had made an error in reporting the results of an early experiment that involved crossing albino mice with house mice, for he kept bringing it up over and over again. Even in this latest criticism of her work, Maud reminded scientists that the albino-house-mice experiment had been done before she had started her cancer research; also, it had been done as a genetic study in collaboration with Professor Charles Otis Whitman. The "error" that Little kept referring to was that after mating an albino to a house mouse, Maud had gotten some gray mice in the first generation, whose later strains did not produce any albinos. Little had pounced on this "error" and had first used it to cast doubt on Maud's early cancer research.

As for Little's admonition that Maud was raising false hopes with her persistent statement that cancer susceptibility was due to a recessive character, Maud replied that a recessive character was certainly involved in the inheritance of cancer susceptibility. She countered Little's statement by saying that to announce that cancer susceptibility was due to a dominant character would cause more harm than informing the public that it was due to a recessive character. Many generations of human beings would have to pass before there could be even the beginning of the fear of such a danger. But the day of profound alarm was now with them. This "cancerphobia" was something the medical profession had to fight.

Little had also questioned Maud's totals, that is, her listing of cancerous mice to establish her conclusions. He pointed out that there had been errors in her charts, mainly duplications of mice. Maud stated that she never directed or geared her work toward totals until after she had done the final analysis of every part of the material. What she had published were preliminary totals, not final totals. She asserted that the counts she had made were open to checking. She could have made far more beneficial selections for her charts, to help establish her theory, but she had been interested in special factors and not in totals. To make certain that her ultimate totals would be correct, she had made it a practice to keep all the mice that died available for postmortem examination only by her. She did not send them, as other researchers did, to the hundreds of scientists who asked for them, both in the United States and abroad. Only by keeping her mice and examining them herself was it possible for her to amass final and accurate totals.

Maud felt that Dr. Little had made an error himself when, in classifying her mice, he had used only a portion of her theory, omitting a very vital part of it. He had not taken account of the hybrid noncancerous mice that would have been derived in the first generation from every cross between a purebred noncancerous mouse and a cancerous mouse if the genetic factor in cancer was recessive, as Maud maintained it was. In testing her theory, Little called all noncancerous mice as such without paying any attention to the distinction that Maud clearly made between *hybrid* and *purebred* mice. The distinction was crucial to any analysis. The hybrid mice would not show the same behavior in heredity as purebred mice. Therefore, argued Maud, a new theory that takes account of only a portion of the original theory had no value.

Dr. Little's theory of cancer susceptibility (that it was due to a dominant character, heterozygous type) showed about 65 percent error, pointed out Maud, and therefore was untenable. The theory of heterozygous dominant cancer was impossible, for in matings demonstrated by Maud, hybrid noncancerous mice crossed with hybrid noncancerous mice showed 94 cancers too few. If cancer was due to a dominant character, as Dr. Little said it was, then the noncancerous mice (that is, hybrid noncancerous) would, according to Maud's theory, be recessive. Also, theoretically, they would not have been able to produce any dominant or cancerous mice, whereas, out of such crosses, 94 cancerous individuals did appear. The fact that any cancerous mice were derived from such crosses between two recessives—in a theory where noncancer was thought to be a recessive character—nullified the whole theory of cancer being due to a dominant character, even allowing for the pure assumption that the cancer was of the heterozygous type only: for two recessive characters could never produce a dominant character.

On the other hand, persisted Maud, her theory that cancer susceptibility was due to a simple recessive character showed less than 10 percent of error, as opposed to the 65 percent of

Dr. Little's dominant character theory. The 10-percent error depended chiefly, if not entirely, on the mice that died from intercurrent conditions before cancer had appeared. The reason for this was that there would always be, in experiments, fewer cancers than those in the classic requirements of a theory. Furthermore, throughout the entire series of experiments there was no conflict with the theory of cancer being due to a recessive character, except that too few cancers had actually appeared from some types of crossmatings. But, said Maud, this was easily explained by the multiplicity of pathologic conditions that caused mice to die before cancer appeared, so that mice that were potentially susceptible to cancer had to be classified as noncancerous.

> I think, [said Maud] that a theory of heredity which shows less than 10 percent of error (as hers did), in so difficult a subject as cancer, comes amazingly close to the requirement, especially when it is tested by a cross section of work not intended to show totals, but selected at random so far as totals are concerned. It is interesting to note that President Little has made no attempt to line up his theory of sex-limited dominance with my figures, *which certainly do not support it.*

Maud stressed the fact that she had repeatedly pointed out that in deciding the nature of the genetic factor in cancer, it was necessary to take account of the known facts of human pathology. If cancer susceptibility was dominant—either by a unit or by a multiple factor, either sex-limited or not, and even if by assumption cancer was called heterozygous dominant—every father with cancer of the stomach, intestines, throat, mouth, or tongue, mated to a noncancerous mother, would produce offspring, in which 50 percent would develop these types of cancer. But, said Maud, this simply was not true, either in the case of experimental animals or in human beings. And the facts of this statement had been established beyond argument. Similarly, if breast cancer was due to a "sex-limited" dominant character, as Dr. Little maintained, every mother with breast cancer would have daughters with breast cancer in at least 50 percent of the cases, and 50 percent of her sons would transmit breast cancer. Not true, stated Maud, for if cancer susceptibility were due to a homozygous dominant character, then the figures would be 100 percent.

Despite Dr. Little's claims, Maud stated that the incidence of cancer in human beings, with their generally hybrid matings, came very close to the expectation for a simple Mendelian recessive character as being the cause of cancer susceptibility. The difficulty that the medical profession had encountered in obtaining data to prove the genetic factor in human cancer was explained by the fact that the genetic character was *recessive*, and that sons and daughters of one cancerous parent and one noncancerous parent do not, in general, show cancer. They would show cancer in 50 percent of cases if the genetic factor were heterozygous dominant, as Dr. Little believed, asserted Maud. Under his theory, there could never be cancerous sons or daughters from parents that had had no cancer. These noncancerous individuals would be 100 percent noncancerous, according to Little's theory. But cancerous sons or daughters from cancer-free parents *was the constant experience in human pathology*. This was explained by Maud's theory of cancer being due to a simple Mendelian recessive character, for then the two noncancerous parents would be hybrids and thus would transmit cancer susceptibility to 25 percent of their offspring.

Maud could not accept Dr. Little's theory that cancer susceptibility was due to a dominant character. In an article published in the *Journal of Cancer Research*, she alluded to the hopelessness which *his* theory evoked:

President Little's theory that the inheritance factor in cancer is dominant is so hopeless for the human race, and for the allaying of cancerphobia, that I am sure all humanity would pray that he may be wrong; and we shall require every proof and conviction that he is not wrong before we accept his theory, which would be so disastrous to human hope of relief. We shall therefore want the most conclusive evidence from him, with the most rigorous insistence that his figures shall be in harmony with his theory, without any assumptions, and *without any conflict with the very basis of all hereditary theory; namely, that two recessives can never produce the dominant.*

And to all of Maud's arguments and explanations, Dr. Little replied, "Poppycock!"

Each of these two highly competent and dedicated cancer researchers persisted that his and her theory of cancer susceptibility was the correct one. The controversy over whether cancer was due to a recessive or dominant character continued in the medical and scientific journals. Major newspapers occasionally ran articles on the subject, emphasizing the different theories. *The New York Times* published photographs of Maud Slye and Clarence Cook Little, side by side on the page, with the main caption: "Rivals in Cancer Research." Under Maud's photo was a statement: "After breeding more than 140,000 mice, Dr. Maud Slye concludes that susceptibility to cancer is transmitted from generation to generation by single hereditary units which determine the type of cancer and its location. She holds that cancer can be bred out." And under Dr. Little's photo was this statement: "Dr. C. C. Little deduces from his thousands of experiments that breast cancer is not transmitted in the Mendelian fashion by genes, but by something that lies outside the chromosomes in which the genes [hereditary units] are packed like peas in a pod."

Unfortunately, both Maud Slye and Clarence Cook Little conducted their cancer and inheritance research at a time when DNA was still an unknown quantity.

TWELVE

One of Clarence Cook Little's complaints about Maud Slye and her cancer research was that the results of her experiment had not been duplicated in any other laboratory. Such duplication, of course, was a prerequisite for the acceptance of any new theory or hypothesis. Maud offered to send some of her cancerous and noncancerous mice to Dr. Little, who now was the director of the Roscoe B. Jackson Memorial Laboratory at Bar Harbor, Maine. However, Little did not take up her offer.

Undaunted, Maud went on with her research and continued to issue reports on the nature of the genetic factor in cancer. She was constantly confronted with the question: What have mouse tumors to do with cancerous growths in human beings? And she patiently explained that mouse cancers were almost identical to those found in human beings as far as type, organs involved, and the clinical course of the disease were concerned. The development of cancer at six months of age in a mouse corresponded roughly to cancer development in a thirty-year-old human being.

She was still highly critical of the American Society for the Control of Cancer, the organization that had assumed the responsibility for disseminating knowledge about cancer. The Society had not, except for the white paper issued after the convention at Lake Mohonk, New York, nearly eight years before, made a positive statement as to the role that heredity played in the incidence of cancer. The white paper,

165

of course, had only suggested that heredity might be a factor in cancer.

Ever since the white-paper episode at Lake Mohonk, Maud and the Society had been involved in a kind of feud in which the weapons were criticisms and denunciations. Members of the Society argued that even if Maud was right, even if it turned out that cancer was hereditary—and the Society did not think that Maud had proved this to be true—passing that knowledge along to the public would cause all kinds of difficulty, not to mention causing people to abandon all hope. Thus, even if Maud's hypothesis was correct, it was better to "let sleeping dogs lie."

Maud could not accept this argument. She repeatedly told the medical profession that there was another factor involved in the development of cancer, irritation. Her first report on cancer and heredity mentioned that irritation was a factor in the incidence of cancer. In that report, she had stated that "hereditary strains of mice determine whether or not a given irritation shall produce cancer."

She also could not accept the pessimistic outlook that the Society claimed would result from a public announcement that cancer was an inheritable disease. The relationship between cancer and heredity did not have to be a cause of pessimism. A person might descend from a cancer-susceptible family, but if the irritation factor was absent, that person might never develop tumors. This fact, said Maud, eliminated the fatalistic claim, put forth by physicians who were opposed to her theory, that members of cancerous families must inevitably develop cancer. She stressed the fact that where there was a history of cancer in a family, special care should be taken to avoid all types of chronic irritation, such as unhealed wounds, jagged teeth, lacerations from childbearing, and similar sources of irritation. Any and all of these conditions should be immediately eliminated. For this reason, Maud declared from the lecture platform and in print, the public should be informed about the facts obtained from her mouse research. And the public should be warned about chronic irritation, particularly that segment of the public belonging to cancerous families.

But the issues remained unresolved. The cancer-research field continued to be divided into schisms or camps that embraced one theory or the other as to the cause of cancer. One group contended that cancer was caused by viruses; another claimed that the lack of or failure to utilize certain vitamins was the causative factor in cancer incidence, whereas the researchers looking into the genetic factors of cancer incidence were split into two factions: supporters of Dr. Little's theory that cancer susceptibility was due to a dominant character and those who agreed with Maud Slye that cancer susceptibility was due to a simple Mendelian recessive character.

When not involved in writing her research reports or answering her growing amount of mail, Maud turned to her poetry. She had collected a number of her poems and sent them off to a publisher. Her first book of poetry was published in 1934 by the Stratford Company in Boston. For this first book of poems, Maud had chosen the title *Songs and Solaces.* In it were the poems she had written over the past twenty years, whenever she had a few hours of respite from the exacting work of the mouse laboratory. She had divided the poems into three groups, with the subtitles; "Of Life," "Of Love," and "Of Science." These were the poems that told of her work, of her frustrations, dreams, yearnings, and disappointments, her intense love of life, her deep interest in nature, her passion for music, and her fascination with the great city of Chicago.

The publication of her book of poetry caused a small ripple of interest among the members of the University of Chicago community. Some scientists wondered if Maud Slye's poetry would get a better reception than her theory on cancer inheritance had received.

The Chicago Daily News and Sun-Times ran a short item on the publication of *Songs and Solaces:*

DR. MAUD SLYE MIXES
POETRY AND SCIENCE

Professor Maud Slye, internationally known authority on cancer and research worker in the Sprague Memorial Institute, whose home of 12,000 mice is a showplace of the Univiersity of Chicago, became known on the campus as a poet.

One advance copy of her first published book of verse, *Songs and Solaces* (Stratford) appeared in the window of the university book store. So far, it is the only copy which has reached Chicago.

When asked to outline her "poetic viewpoint," Maud warned her interviewers against looking for any complete philosophy in her book of poetry. "Poetry is not a mere vehicle for putting over philosophies or religious views," she said. She went on to explain that there was as yet no complete philosophy of science. "We know something in biology. We know something in chemistry. We know something in the realm of physics. But we have not as yet dovetailed all these bodies of knowledge into a complete philosophy. It is unscientific to pretend that we have — and it is unscientific to say what that philosophy will be when we do achieve it. But I have faith that it will be fully adequate to our needs as human beings."

Maud expounded on the need of scientists to work in or relate to other fields of life. "The imagination by which the scientist works should be given scope in other fields, if the scientist is to remain alive and fully human," she told students, faculty members, and reporters. "It is not strange that a scientist should also be a poet. Einstein plays the violin. Michelson was a painter. Eddington writes on mystical and religious themes. My poetry is an attempt to paint in words. It is not to be taken as self-revelatory. I have written of what I have seen, felt, and thought."

Although Maud insisted that her poetry was not self-revelatory, her poems did indeed reveal much about this multitalented woman. Granted, analysis is never a substitute for a poem. Yet a poem may be said to be a formal structure composed of various elements that function at the same time. Thus, in any analysis of poetry, each element must be discussed separately. By isolating for special consideration some of the many simultaneous elements of Maud Slye's poems, a little of the nature of the poet is revealed. Even in the most objective writing, something of the writer comes forth; the repetitive use of a word or phrase can be self-revelatory for the writer. Maud certainly was more subjective in her poetry than in her scientific papers and reports. As she herself said, she wrote about what she had seen, felt, and thought. And what she had seen, felt, and thought were things, people, and events that had made a deep impression on her or left hidden scars. While Maud would not admit it, her poetry did reveal quite a bit about Maud Slye, the scientist, artist, and human being.

In August of 1936, Maud decided to combine a vacation with business. Her hair was grayer now and her face seemed to be carved from granite. She had a slight stoop to her shoulders, a result of the years of bending over mouse cages and microscopes. But she had not lost any of her ardor or determination; her eyes still flashed fire when she defended her cancer-inheritance theory. Now she would have the opportunity to explain and defend her work on a worldwide plane at the International Congress for the Control of Cancer in Brussels. But even though she would be lecturing, the trip abroad would still be a vacation for her—the first in more than twenty-five years.

In addition to the International Congress for the Control of Cancer in Brussels, Maud lectured to physicians and scientists in Amsterdam, Berlin, Paris, and London. Her lectures were received with a mixture of curiosity, prejudice, and hostility by audiences dominated by male physicians and scientists. In Brussels, she told the assembly of distinguished physicians and scientists of her work in the mouse laboratory in Chicago. She discussed the case histories of 5,000 cancerous and non-cancerous mice as they related to the inheritability of cancer. She detailed the more than 138,000 autopsies she had conducted on her mice. She described how she could walk through her mouse laboratory, glance at the case histories of each of the 9,000 mice living there, and predict what kind of cancer, if any, each mouse would develop. Furthermore, she could tell ninety-eight times out of a hundred how soon a tumor would appear and in what part of a mouse's body.

Physicians and scientists in Brussels, Amsterdam, Berlin, Paris, and London listened attentively as the slight, gray-haired woman lectured to them on the inheritability of cancer. Many of them forgot for the moment or simply put aside their various objections to Maud Slye's theory. The obvious dedication of this woman scientist to her research, her fantastic feat of carefully conducting autopsies on thousands of mice, and her animated delivery of her work and findings brought forth nods of approval from the members of her audiences, despite the highly controversial nature of the material.

In each of the cities she visited, Maud told the physicians and scientists that the susceptibility to cancer was due to a simple Mendelian recessive character, transmitted by a single gene. Resistance to cancer was due to a dominant character, which repressed but did not obliterate the susceptibility factor whenever they occurred together. A cancer-resistant individual mated to a susceptible one would have cancer-resistant offspring. But these offspring would carry the cancer suscep- tibility gene concealed in their germ plasm, and if they mated with cancer-susceptible individuals, the second generation would be liable to develop cancer.

She emphasized over and over again that her experiments showed that some injury or irritation factor was necessary for the development of malignant tumors. She described how some of her mice that were susceptibile to cancer of the jaw did not develop it when she kept their teeth filed down to prevent chronic irritation. Everywhere she lectured, she re- newed her plea for the establishment of a bureau of human cancer statistics. "If we had records for human beings compa- rable to those for mice," she told the audiences, "we could stamp out cancer in a generation. Sweden has made a start . . . but no other country in the world is making such an effort. Meanwhile, cancer is a leading cause of death, and as we make progress in heart diseases, it is likely to become the first cause in a comparatively short time."

Although Maud made an impression on many members of her audiences or seminars, some of whom were calling her the "American Curie," there was still a hard core of physicians and scientists who, like their counterparts in America, re- fused to accept Maud's conclusions. As was the case in America, cancer researchers in Europe were divided into camps, each of which espoused a different theory as to the causes of cancer. Viruses and vitamin deficiency were the prime suspects as the causative factor in cancer, and for those European cancer researchers who did go along with the ge- netic factor, most of them agreed with Clarence Cook Little that cancer susceptibility was due to a dominant, not a reces- sive character, as claimed by Maud Slye.

When Maud returned to the United States, she found that her absence had not put the lid on the cancer inheritance controversy, at least not as far as Clarence Cook Little was concerned. Little, when interviewed by the medical correspondent for *Time* magazine, severely criticized Maud Slye and her research. "It has always seemed to me a great pity that some neutral and properly qualified laboratory should not make a very simple test of the correctness of Miss Slye's hypothesis concerning the recessive Mendelian inheritance of all types of cancer," said Little. He added, "If the matter could not be tested easily, there would be some excuse for continuing the publication of contradictory [meaning Maud's] evidence."

Little again called on Maud Slye to give, lend, or sell to some neutral laboratory or institution a herd of male mice that she could vouch for as having no tendency to cancer. If Maud would do this, he would give one thousand of his cancer-susceptible female mice for breeding to Maud's cancer-free mice at a mutually acceptable and neutral institution. Later, the offspring from these matings would be bred, brother to sister.

> If cancer appears in any of the hybrid females [stated Dr. Little], then Miss Slye's theory is incorrect and the type of inheritance is not simply Mendelian, nor is it cancer recessive. The test should take from two to three years, but is so direct and simple, involving only elementary principles of Mendelian inheritance and no permanent removal of any of Miss Slye's animals from her laboratory, that I cannot see why it should not be supported and begin at once. If Miss Slye's theory is correct, its importance as a practical matter to the human race is great. If it is incorrect, it is high time to recognize that fact generally and end the controversy.

But Maud had had enough of Dr. Little's public offers to her to submit some of her mice to a test. When pressed for her response to Little's latest challenge, she told the *Time* magazine reporter that she could not be bothered with Dr. Little's challenge to test the validity of her cancer theory.

When queried about the unfavorable impression her refusal to accept Little's challenge would make in the scientific community, not to mention the general public, Maud told the reporter that it would be pointless to submit to the test since the nontumorous strains of mice with which she had started her long experiment and with which she had expanded her research, were no longer in existence. Then she added tartly, "Some five years ago, I offered to make this test. I drew up a contract for this experiment and I submitted it to Dr. Little. To this offer I received no reply and the matter was dropped." And Maud's firm gaze convinced the *Time* reporter that the matter would remain dropped; more than that, it was dead and buried as far as Maud Slye was concerned.

Dr. Little's contention that more than one genetic factor was involved in cancer inheritance seemed to be supported by new studies that he and other researchers had undertaken. Maud now found herself in a decision-making position: she could either stick to her original conclusion that cancer susceptibility was due to a single Mendelian recessive character—in the face of mounting evidence to the contrary—or go back over her vast collection of data and mouse-cancer records and revise her conclusion in light of recent studies. She opted to revise her conclusion.

Maud presented her revised theory and conclusion at the twenty-second annual meeting of the Radiological Society of North America in Cincinnati, Ohio, in December of 1936. She was now the director of the Cancer Laboratory, Sprague Memorial Institute, and Associate Professor of Pathology at the University of Chicago. She also was the recipient of a number of awards, including the American Medical Association Gold Medal, the Ricketts Prize from the university, and a Gold Medal from the Radiological Society. The paper that she delivered before the Radiological Society was entitled "The Relation of Heredity to the Occurrence of Cancer."

She began her presentation to the members of the Radiological Society with an appeal:

I beg that you will give attention to the charts that I shall present and not look upon them as a piece of work of academic interest only, for they show and explain the breeding out of breast cancer through nine generations of mice. This complete elimination of breast cancer from an entire family of mice tested through so many generations is highly significant when one considers the fact that breast cancer is so overwhelmingly the cancer menace of mice that geneticists and research workers, other than myself, rarely report upon any other forms of mouse malignancy. In terms of human life, these nine generations would mean over six hundred years of complete freedom from breast cancer, and the exemptions from cancer that I have observed in some strains of mice throughout the twenty-seven years of this work would, in terms of human experience, mean a freedom from cancer of some three thousand years.

She went on to tell the attentive radiologists that cancer was not an academic problem maintained for the bickerings of some geneticists who did not happen to agree on this or that detail of the method of cancer heredity. This, of course, was aimed at Clarence Cook Little, Francis Carter Wood, and the other geneticists and scientists who had not agreed with Maud's work and conclusions. Cancer was a social problem, continued Maud, a vast social menace, and it was time something was done to stop its increase before it moved up to be the first cause of all human deaths. It was to such an end that she had gone on with her research despite all the controversy and criticisms, both personal and professional, that her work had met from certain quarters of the scientific community.

Maud explained her revised theory of cancer inheritance. Apparently two causes were operative in the production of cancers: inherited susceptibility and irritation or chronic stimulation by particular hormones, carcinogenic agents, or trauma. In mice resistant by heredity to cancer, irritations and trauma incident to life in her mouse laboratory had never induced cancer, whereas in mice susceptible by heredity to only one location of cancer, irritation or stimulation applied to other parts of the body had so far failed to induce neoplasms in these susceptible tissues.

In some studies, when irritation to locally susceptible tissues had been avoided, cancer did not even occur in susceptible strains of mice. For example, uneven teeth were common in her mice; consequently, the jagged teeth struck upon the soft tissues of the mouth and jaw. In her observation, this seemed to be one of the possible external factors that induced cancers of these tissues. Many mice in cancer-susceptible strains had developed malignancy at the point of contact of such teeth. But she had not yet determined whether the crooked or jagged teeth were the first cause of this cancer relationship.

In carcinoma-susceptible mice the result was carcinoma. In nonsusceptible strains the result was never malignancy, but only inflammatory or septic changes in the tissues. It seemed possible to Maud to prevent such cancers in susceptible mice by keeping their teeth short, thus preventing the constant traumatism of the soft mouth and jaw tissues. She emphasized that by keeping the teeth short in cancer-susceptible mice it had been possible to prevent mouth and jaw cancer. This fact seemed to demonstrate that the irritation factor was influential as an accelerator or external causative agent of cancer.

Maud next presented a report on an entire strain of mice, comprising 650 individuals, derived from the original mating of two individuals, and carefully analyzed by inbreeding for nine generations. The object of this study had been to determine the behavior of malignancy as a biologic character and to demonstrate the influence and method of heredity in the occurrence of malignancy and its localization. She displayed charts and records on these mice. She reminded the radiologists that the tumors produced in these mice had not been induced by any experimental procedures whatever. They were all spontaneous tumors, arising naturally in the life of the mice and developing without any interference of any sort, at any time.

Every mouse had been permitted to live out its natural life span and thus show all of its natural cancer tendencies and all of the systemic changes wrought by cancer. No mouse was killed. Since the death of the first mouse in this study, Maud had autopsied every mouse as soon as possible after death and had examined histologically every suspicious tissue for malignancy. The tissues and slides from this study were now part of a permanent museum and on display for all to see. Every precaution had been taken to see that no mouse was destroyed by postmortem changes. To this end, all mice were examined at least once daily and every sick mouse inspected three times a day. No mouse had ever been discarded without first being subjected to an autopsy. No cancers were reported without confirmed microscopic diagnoses of malignancy. Thus, Maud had taken every precaution against any chance for error.

"I wish to remind you," Maud told the radiologists, "that whatever reports are made concerning the experimental production of tumors by various agents, there are included in my studies close to a hundred thousand individual tumors in mice to which nothing has been done. These spontaneous tumors will have to be taken into account in the consideration of any experimentally applied external agent as the efficient cause of cancer."

Then Maud went on to her revised conclusion on the mode of cancer inheritance. Malignancy was an abnormal type of cell growth transmitted as a localized recessive character, each type of malignancy being a unit character and capable of suppression by a dominant allele. There was, said Maud, a different unit of recessive character for each type of cancer, as well as a different unit for each local site where cancer occurred.

Consequently, cancer would be caused by a *different* unit of recessive genetic factor *for each type of malignancy* (for instance, carcinoma, sarcoma, leukemia, etc.), not just by a single-unit character for all types of malignancy, as Maud had previously postulated. In addition, there had to be a unit of recessive genetic factor *for each local site* of malignancy for that particular type of cancer (mammary-gland tumor, lung tumor, etc). External causative factors, perhaps environmental or intraorganic, also had to be considered, as well as special metabolic relationships.

Maud explained that nonoccurrence of cancer where it was expected might be due to several factors. Chief among them was that only one recessive factor existed. *The recessive factor for type of malignancy and the recessive localizing factor must both occur together.* Other important factors were lack of exposure to the necessary external factors; unfavorable metabolic conditions, such as intercurrent and degenerative diseases; and finally, a short life span that prevented an individual from reaching cancer age.

Maud told the radiologists that she was happy to announce that all geneticists now working in cancer research agreed there was a hereditary basis in malignant disease. All cancer research in the late 1930's was founded on the hereditary theory. Furthermore, strains of mice different in their cancer susceptibilities, such as those strains developed in her mouse laboratory, were vital for cancer research.

Maud was also glad that many of the outstanding members of the medical profession now accepted the demonstrated fact of cancer susceptibility. But now it was necessary to think of how to apply this knowledge on a practical basis.

"What shall we do?" she asked the intent audience of radiologists. "I have been telling the medical profession for sixteen years—and Karl Pearson of England [British researcher] before me, repeatedly made the same plea—that is, a plea for human records. I am here to make that plea again and to remind you that the necessity for human records is the same, irrespective of any details of a genetic theory; indeed, they would in time prove the correctness or the error of any genetic theory, and they would be the court of last appeal."

Maud jogged the memories of the radiologists, telling them that she had spoken at some of their previous meetings about the need to set up a bureau of human cancer statistics, but they, like other branches of the medical profession, had done nothing about it. All the more lamentable, she added, because cancer had now become the second leading cause of human deaths in the United States.

Like the others [she said], you perhaps think we can do nothing to breed out cancer. Before Pasteur's work was accepted, and before Florence Nightingale's work was done, nobody thought there was any such truth about infections which placed them within control, and everybody scoffed at aseptic wounds and hospitals. Now these things are commonplace and have become routine procedures.

I am willing to admit [she continued], that any step actually to breed out cancer may lie far ahead, but the glory will be to those who . . . do it. And when it is done, it also will be a routine procedure. If specific types and sites of tumors can be ruled out of mouse families, they can be ruled out of human families. We can make possible this future procedure by the simple method of taking adequate records now, and assembling them in a control bureau where they can be of service. Moreover, there is a manner in which these records will be of immediate value, and in which you yourselves can use them. They will be of immeasurable and immediate diagnostic value.

Maud's reconciliation of her original conclusion about cancer inheritability with newer findings more or less ended her great research project. She had unquestionably proved that there was a link between cancer and inheritance, thus providing an important weapon with which to fight cancer. What the medical profession now had to do was to apply the findings of Maud Slye, Clarence Cook Little, Francis Carter Wood, and the other cancer researchers.

The proposed bureau of human cancer statistics should have been the next step in the battle against malignant diseases. Maud, now nearing sixty years of age, continued to plead for the establishment of such a statistical research angency. "If we could inaugurate a system of records for humans," she stated in her public appearances and interviews, "we could—over a period of years—eliminate cancer because we would have the knowledge of what causes it, both hereditary factors and the external factors, and therefore we would know how to avoid it. The medical bureau of cancer statistics would embrace the knowledge of the patient, to complement the science of knowledge of the disease."

But the accumulation of human cancer statistics would have to be done on a statewide and state-by-state basis. "Imagine," said Maud, "the invaluable information we would have on cancer if such a system were on a statewide basis, and if every state had such a bureau. Every hospital and every physician could cooperate. The press and the radio could aid immeasurably. Look what has been done in the study of syphilis!" She added that the data and records amassed in the cancer-statistic bureau would settle the cause of cancer.

A cancer-statistics collection bureau, as envisioned by Maud Slye, never did materialize. Other than a code system devised by Maud Slye for the Cook County Hospital in Chicago, little was done in this important area of cancer research. Maud kept crusading for the bureau, but time was running out on her. Now that her primary research had been completed, the University of Chicago began to wind down the Sprague Memorial Institute's sponsorship. Maud's funds were cut off, and the university planned to take over her mouse laboratory for another purpose.

The loss of the research sponsorship and funds was a big blow to Maud. She still had several thousand mice to maintain, and there was food to buy. Her own resources were meager, hardly enough to take care of her own needs. The only course left to her was to let her mice die off. She could not bring herself to kill her animals. Instead, she chose to let them live out their life spans, which would be short for the cancerous mice and long for the cancer-resistant mice. To purchase food and other supplies, she cashed in her life-insurance policy and liquidated what other few assets she possessed.

Week after week, she watched her mouse colony dwindle down. She went on with her work, carefully collating and interpretating the mass of data she had accumulated over more than thirty years—thirty years that had been filled with frustrations, disappointments, criticisms, and little triumphs. But they had been productive years. True, she had not discovered a cure for cancer, but then that had never been her goal, as it had been that of Clarence Cook Little. She had set out to learn if there was a relationship between cancer and inheritance. And she had demonstrated, after years of work and privation, that there were indeed genetic factors involved in the incidence of cancer.

In 1944, at the age of sixty-five, Maud Slye was automatically retired from the faculty of the University of Chicago. All of her mice were gone now, and the old mouse laboratory on Drexel Avenue had been taken over by another department. All that was left of the great research project that had spanned so many years and had stirred the world of cancer research was a pile of data and records.

A lifetime of work was now stored in boxes, and all that Maud had left of her beloved mouse laboratory was the view of the building from her home across the street. She had written long ago that the mouse laboratory was a ray of light which penetrated the darkness enveloping the field of cancer research. Now that light had gone out. Her work was done.

> Well, I have given all my work,
> Now let it stand or fall.
> Let it be pierced with the divining dirk,
> Or let it live through all.

Ten years later, the Mouse Lady was dead. By that time, physicians were asking their patients if anyone in their family had had cancer.

Glossary

Allele—one of the two alternative forms of a gene

Benign—noncancerous

Biometrician—a scientist who analyzes biological data by mathematical methods

Carcinoma—a malignant tumor of epithelial origin

Chromosomes—the bodies in the cell nucleus that contain genes

Complementary genes—two or more genes whose combined effect is qualitatively different from the separate effect of any one of them

Congenital—acquired during development in the uterus and not through heredity

Dominant trait—one of a pair of alleles that suppresses expression of the other in the heterozygous condition

Endemic condition—one that persists within a particular community

Epithelial tissue—tissue covering all body surfaces that may be exposed to foreign substances, such as the skin or the inside of the digestive tract

Eugenics—the scientific study of the improvement of hereditary qualities of a race or breed

Extracted strain—one produced by controlled or selective breeding

Gamete—a mature reproductive cell

Gene—a hereditary unit consisting of a pair of alleles

Genetics—the scientific study of heredity and variation in organisms

Heredity—the transmission of qualities from ancestor to descendant through the genes

Heterozygous—the condition that exists when the alleles of a gene are different

Homozygous—the condition that exists when the alleles of a gene are the same

Hybrid—a heterozygous plant or animal

In utero—in the uterus

In vitro—within a test tube

Malignant—cancerous

Mesodermal tissue—the tissue layer forming bone, cartilage, and muscle

Metastasis—the spreading of cancerous cells throughout the body via the blood or lymph channels

Necropsy—postmortem examination

Neoplasm—tumor, either benign or cancerous

Recessive trait—one that is dormant when suppressed by the dominant trait, but is expressed when in the homozygous condition

Sarcoma—a malignant tumor of mesodermal origin

Selective breeding—breeding by selection of the mates; not breeding randomly

Sex chromosome—the two chromosomes that together determine the sex of an organism

Sex-limited—located in a sex chromosome

Sex-linked—occurring in only one sex

Simple Mendelian character—one that follows Mendel's first law of heredity regarding dominant and recessive traits

Spontaneous tumor—a tumor that develops naturally and is not grafted on or produced by the introduction of a foreign substance

Toxin—a poisonous substance

Tumor—a new growth of tissue serving no physiological function

Index

DATE DUE

GAYLORD			PRINTED IN U.S.A.